ENDORSEMENTS

"I recently learned that yoga means 'unity' in Sanskrit. The Simpkins have un ....ly, if ever, been pulled together: yoga (not just the body moves, but the deeper psychological, emotional, and spiritual aspects as well), mindfulness practices, and therapeutic methods. Joining them together in a practical way can help relieve stress, anxiety, mood problems, and substance abuse challenges.

"You can use these methods for yourself or, if you work with others as a therapist, medical practitioner, or coach, you can use them with clients. [It is] filled with exercises, tips, and inspiring stories."

—Bill O'Hanlon, featured Oprah guest and author of *Out of the Blue:*
Six Non-Medication Ways to Relieve Depression

"*The Yoga and Mindfulness Therapy Workbook* offers a treasure trove of resources and practical exercises that are perfect for anyone wanting a unified mind-body approach to finding greater emotional focus, stability, balance, and ease in life. The timeless truths offered of yoga and mindfulness are seamlessly blended with modern brain science and research to provide solid evidence for why these practices can overcome 21st century stress, anxiety, and depression. The compelling real-life stories throughout the book illustrate that change really *is* possible! Most importantly, the expertly detailed exercises and many guided illustrations will have you feeling that authors Alex and Annellen Simpkins are right beside you, sharing their years of experience and wisdom, as you step on this path to greater healing and wholeness."

—Donald Altman, M.A., LPC, author *The Mindfulness Toolbox,*
One-Minute Mindfulness, and *The Mindfulness Code*

"*The Yoga and Mindfulness Therapy Workbook* is much more than a 'workbook.' It is also a 'sourcebook,' taking its readers into the philosophical foundations of yoga and mindfulness and forward into their neuroscience and psycho-therapeutic applications. The exercises are user-friendly, and their health benefits are documented and explained. The chapters on yogic breathing, cognitive reframing, and self-regulation of attention are practical and articulate. The Drs. Simpkins have written a magnificent volume that attests to their own authority as well as their decades of clinical practice.

—Stanley Krippner, Ph.D., co-author of *Personal Mythology*
and co-editor of *Extraordinary Dreams*

The Yoga and Mindfulness Therapy Workbook

C. ALEXANDER SIMPKINS, PhD

AND

ANNELLEN M. SIMPKINS, PhD

PESI
Publishing
& Media
www.pesipublishing.com

Published by
PESI Publishing & Media
PESI, Inc
3839 White Ave
Eau Claire, WI 54703
Editing: Bookmasters
Layout: Bookmasters
Cover Design: Amy Rubenzer

Printed in the United States of America

ISBN 978-1-936128-83-9

PESI
Publishing
& Media
www.pesipublishing.com

Table of Contents

Introduction

We weave the cloth of our everyday
By what we do and give.
The fabric of our everyway
Is made by how we live.
—C. Alexander Simpkins

At their heart, yoga and mindfulness hold to the idea that you can cultivate well-being by what you do and how you live. Meditation is a practice, something you do to train the mind and body in ways that bring about a shift in consciousness. Recent research has found that practicing these meditative methods changes your brain and rebalances your nervous system. You experience increased calmness and happiness and can regulate your emotions and behavior, goals that psychotherapy aims to foster. Thus, integrating yoga and mindfulness can facilitate the therapeutic process.

Yoga and mindfulness are practices whereby *doing* brings *knowing*; and so, this experiential workbook is intended as something you *do,* which means we encourage you to actively engage with the material. You will find many different ways to get involved that will evoke a variety of experiences. The chapters contain tips to guide you, information boxes to add more details, lists for easy access, exercises to perform, and illustrations to follow. We also supply journaling guidance and charts to fill out, which will provide feedback as you progress. Case examples show how other people have benefited from using these methods, which serve as inspiration for your own change process. We are excited to bring you this practical workbook!

The learning is offered at two levels. First, you will find that the techniques and methods, with explicit and easy-to-follow instructions, elicit a specific change or a particular response. Then, on a deeper level, nonspecific effects, such as experiencing well-being or changes in your energy level, will occur. Through the process, you will learn how to individualize these methods to suit your personal needs.

WHO CAN USE THIS WORKBOOK?

This book speaks directly to the reader: clients in therapy, individuals seeking self-help, or therapists who wish to apply these methods with clients or on themselves. Therapists seeking to use yoga and mindfulness with clients can combine the methods we describe with conventional therapies. In some cases, these practices can be used as a stand-alone approach.

WHAT'S INSIDE

Your *Yoga and Mindfulness Therapy Workbook* is divided into three parts. Part I provides background and preliminary information. Quick tips get you started and answer some of your questions. You will learn about the philosophy that underlies yoga and mindfulness practices, the neuroscience that explains the positive way these methods alter your nervous system, and the research that has shown yoga and mindfulness to be effective methods for therapy. The final chapter in Part I guides you in developing yoga and mindfulness tools: sensory tools, attention tools, and body tools, all of which facilitate practice.

Part II offers clear instructions in the basic practices of yoga and mindfulness. You will learn how to apply the yamas and niyamas (the dos and don'ts of yoga), some basic asanas (postures), and practice pranayama (breathing methods). Meditation skills improve as you learn pratyahara (how to withdraw your attention), dharana (keep your focus where you choose), and dhyana (allow the open free flow of awareness). Mindfulness practice teaches you how to have open focus, changing the object of your focus moment by moment. Case examples show how people have used each of these practices for therapeutic change.

With the knowledge and skills you attained in Part II, you will be ready to apply yoga and mindfulness therapeutically. Part III offers separate chapters for each of the following problems: stress, anxiety, depression, trauma, and substance abuse. We recommend yoga and mindfulness protocols, but we encourage you to use exercises from any or all of the chapters. Experiment, feel your response, and let it develop. Be patient and allow the time that change takes. Your mind-brain-body system will shift as healthier habits form and you find balance. Trust yourself and enjoy the process!

The appendix is for therapists. This section explains how to seamlessly integrate yoga and mindfulness into your treatments. You will find answers to questions you may have about how and when to introduce the techniques, ways to adapt your office, and tips for working with clients. And there are special techniques for children and adolescents who do very well with these methods. You will also find a section specifically designed for therapists' well-being. As helpers of others, we often neglect ourselves, and this part offers easy-to-use methods for our own personal care and actualization.

ABOUT THE AUTHORS

We have been working with these methods for more than 40 years, using them in our own lives and guiding clients in applying them for therapeutic change. We teach yoga and mindfulness workshops to professionals and have written numerous books on Eastern meditation methods and how to use them therapeutically (please see the bibliography). We also teach and write about neuroscience and hypnosis, both of which we have integrated into our clinical work and our teaching seminars around the world. We have conducted psychotherapy research and are currently researching unconscious processes. It is our sincere hope that you will find this workbook helpful, meaningful, and transformative!

Part I

The Why and How to Get You Started

When in worldly activity, keep attentive between the two breaths, and so practicing, in a few days be born anew.

—Malini Vijaya Tantra

In Part I

- Introduction to the philosophies inspiring yoga and mindfulness practices
- How yoga and mindfulness improve brain structures and functions
- Overview of research showing the efficacy of yoga and mindfulness for therapy
- Quick tips to get you started
- The tools you need to delve into your meditative practices

Yoga and mindfulness derive from rich traditions that have enhanced the quality of life and enriched the wisdom of the soul. These practices can be valuable additions to most current forms of therapy. As a mind-body practice, yoga and mindfulness change the brain, alter thinking, balance emotions, open sensory experiencing, and foster awareness. With the ever-growing body of neuroscience and research, you can feel confident in making yoga and mindfulness part of your therapeutic journey.

CHAPTER 1

Foundations in Philosophy, Neuroscience, and Science

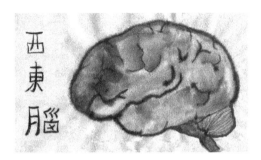

From the roots, we get the essence.

—Zen saying

In This Chapter

- Philosophies of yoga and mindfulness
- Therapeutic effects on the brain, both functional and structural
- Brain changes that all forms of meditation share
- Distinctions between the various meditation practices found in yoga and mindfulness
- Review of the efficacy research

Introduction

Yoga and mindfulness have many positive effects on the mind and body. Their practices lead to a calmer and more alert mind and a healthier and more flexible body. Their healing effects have been experienced for millennia, and give us a rationale for incorporating these practices into psychotherapy. Modern neuroscience provides even more evidence. Research helps to pinpoint the ways yoga and mindfulness are therapeutic. We describe the ancient philosophies and contemporary research. This chapter also provides a strong and well-researched rationale for why yoga and mindfulness are useful interventions to integrate into commonly used therapeutic approaches.

Philosophy

It is light inside, light outside, a light along and holier than holy. It is the light that lights all light, uncaused. And it is the light of the self.

—The Upanishads (ancient Hindu texts)

The West is known for having a practical, behavioral orientation to life. We take pride in doing what is efficient and effective. Pragmatism, a philosophy that guides Western thought, is concerned with what is useful, what works. In the East, the driving effort has been toward enlightenment, higher knowledge, and spirituality. Working together with East and West, you harvest a vast, deep reservoir for psychological growth.

Yoga: Yoking the Mind to Seek Truth

Yoga is restraining the mind-stuff from taking various forms.
At that time, the seer rests in his own (unmodified) state.

— Patañjali in the Eight Limbs of Yoga

Yoga is ageless and timeless. What makes yoga unique is that it is a practical system, not only a philosophy or religion. The result is that you get something out of practicing yoga: health, self-discipline, and raised consciousness.

Yoga disciplines the mind and body by combining physical exercise and meditation. By doing the exercises, you learn how to hold your mind and direct it at will wherever and to whatever you choose.

The word *yoga* means "yoke" or "union." According to yogic tradition, you succeed best when you train persistently, disciplining your mind and body to gain control, yoking mind to body, and withdrawing from the illusory world of the senses. By searching inward, you discover the true knowledge of reality that links you as an individual to something greater—the universal.

Yogic theory, drawn from Hinduism, holds that we all have a soul, or self, called *Atman*. The goal of yoga is to connect Atman to Brahman. Atman is like a drop of water, the individual. Brahman is like the ocean, the universal. Through enlightened knowledge of your true self, your individual soul becomes one with universal consciousness.

FIGURE 1.1 Union: The drop of water returns to the sea.

The Eight Limbs of Yoga

The Eight Limbs are a system codified by Patañjali, in the second century BC. He was careful to point out that he had not created this system, but rather was gathering and organizing wisdom that preexisted for centuries. The Eight Limbs take you on a stepwise journey to reach higher consciousness and inner peace.

- Limbs 1 and 2 (the *yamas* and *niyamas*) change your mental attitude to live morally according to rules of conduct, striving not to engage in harmful actions, while adopting healthy habits. The *yamas* and *niyamas* also guide you in actualizing your potential, to become the best you can be.
- Limb 3 (*pranayama*) controls the breath. *Prana* is universal vital energy. Breath control is the key to taking in and directing the energy of prana for health, vitality, and higher consciousness.

FIGURE 1.2 The Eight Limbs

- Limb 4 *(asana)* involves body postures. The body is the vehicle of the soul, and so the body is as highly valued as the mind. Most people think of yoga as merely postures, but this is only part of the picture. Yoga fosters a mind, body, spirit unity, which includes, but is not limited to, physical postures.

- Limb 5 *(pratyahara)* teaches you how to withdraw your attention from everyday matters to free your consciousness for higher pursuits where the deeper essence of reality is revealed. This skill also has many practical and therapeutic applications, especially when you have to endure something you can't or perhaps shouldn't change.

- Limb 6 *(dharana)* trains you in focused concentration. You learn to keep your attention steady and delve deeply. Restraint through exercising the will is one of the central principles employed in yoga. This control of the *mind stuff*, as Patañjali called it, brings great freedom from the ever-roaming monkey mind that jumps around from thing to thing. As you become the master of your mind, you gain a kind of mind-over-matter power.

- Limb 7 *(dhyana)* is possible after you have mastered the earlier steps. Yoga is freedom. Once you have the ability to control your mind, you can also let it be free. Empty of thoughts and absolutely open, you become like the cosmos.

- Limb 8 *(samadhi, enlightenment)* is the culmination. Yoga practice takes place on three planes: first, the physical; second, the mental (the mind and intellect); and finally, the absolute. In yogic meditation, you become part of the total field of concentration, just as a mirror reflecting the color blue appears blue. Through the discipline of meditation, you acquire health, longevity, and extraordinary powers. A modern yogi, the Swami Rama, demonstrated these powers when he showed Menninger Foundation researchers that he could create atrial flutter (a dangerous accelerated beating of the heart that often leads to blood clots and stroke) with no harmful effects (Green, Green, & Walters, 1970). But these benefits are considered secondary. The highest aim of yoga is enlightenment. By means of the eight limbs, you can unite with the greater whole, the true self.

Mindfulness: Truth Is Mind

Buddha, the originator of mindfulness, started out as a yoga practitioner. Even though he ultimately rejected yogic philosophy, he incorporated many of its principles into his new religion, Buddhism. Much of Buddhist meditation and codes of conduct derive from yoga, and so you will find that the practice of yoga and mindfulness fit well together, giving you a clear path to develop not just your mind, but also your heart, your brain, and your entire body!

Buddha was looking for a way to end suffering. He discovered the solution through his own enlightened meditation, which he shared with the world as the Four Noble Truths.

- The First Truth is that we must recognize suffering and frustration as a part of life. We suffer from pain, sickness, and inevitable death. This is an inescapable truth for all living beings.

- The Second Truth is that this suffering comes from clinging, craving, and grasping. The world seems to offer many comforts and pleasures, but these external things never bring lasting happiness.

- The Third Truth reveals that the cause of suffering can be eliminated when we give up craving for pleasures and comforts and expecting them to last. Nothing endures, all is transitory, and recognizing this truth can set us free.

- Finally, the way to let go of these cravings is to follow the Eightfold Path, the Fourth Truth. This path is a therapeutic journey of eight steps.

  □ The first two steps on the path—right views and right aspirations—involve understanding the human condition.

  □ The next four—right speech, right behavior, right livelihood, and right effort—entail abandoning unwholesome entanglements and living a healthy lifestyle.

FIGURE 1.3 Buddha

  □ The final two—right thoughts and right contemplation—include developing the skills of mindfulness and meditation, the inner mental practice that brings an end to suffering and the cultivation of wisdom. Like Socrates of ancient Greece, Buddha valued wisdom as the highest good.

Mindfulness Practice

Meditation is an effective pathway to wisdom. Truth is found through the mind, detached from the problems of everyday life. And yet, truth is not something like the typical things we seek. The fundamental idea of mindfulness may seem foreign to the Western way of thinking. We are accustomed to putting things into concepts and hierarchies in order to know them. But mindfulness gives you another tool for knowing yourself and the world. As Buddha taught, truth is "undeclared." The practice of mindfulness will take you to this "undeclared" truth, a wordless insight that is beyond rational thought. Paradoxically, by nonconceptual, nonrational mindful practice, you attain deep knowledge of yourself and the world.

Mindfulness is an approach to life, a way of orienting yourself with alert awareness and complete presence. The word *mindfulness* implies its meaning: mind FULLness is a method for filling the mind so fully and completely with each moment that it becomes empty of any distractions or extraneous thoughts. Mindfulness is not just a matter of *what* you do or think, but rather *how* you apply your mental attention and involvement. You use your body, feelings, and thoughts. In time, your awareness spreads into every moment, like a light that illuminates the darkness, to reveal a vast vista of potential for wisdom, freedom, and compassion.

RESEARCH: HOW YOGA AND MINDFULNESS CHANGE THE BRAIN

You have seen how yoga and mindfulness transform the mind, but these practices also change the brain in both its functions and structures. For example, a study using mindfulness showed an increase in regional gray matter density (Hotzel et al., 2011). These structural changes were located in an important brain area for psychological health, the anterior cingulate gyrus. This part of the brain helps to monitor conflicts and regulate emotions. Deficits in this brain area have been associated with depression, ADHD, and schizophrenia. Hotzel's research and many other studies will be described in this section to show you what neuroscience is teaching us about meditation's helpful therapeutic influence.

What All Forms of Meditation Share

Dual Effect: Neuroscience studies have revealed an interesting effect of regular meditation practice: It both activates and relaxes the nervous system simultaneously, that is, the mind and body relax while attention and perception are sharpened (Bhatia et al. 2003).

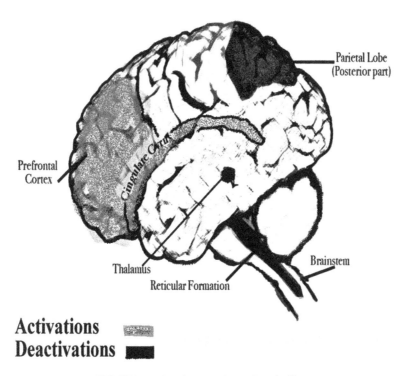

Activations
Deactivations

FIGURE 1.4 Meditating Brain Dual Effect

If you pay close attention to something, you tense up as your brain is stimulated. By contrast, when you meditate, you are highly alert and aware, and yet, simultaneously, you tend to have a low heart rate and slow breathing, qualities of relaxation. You gain the ability to direct your attention to whatever is needed without being tense.

- Relaxation: Researchers have long known that meditation is superior to simply resting for calming the nervous system. When you practice meditation, you activate a relaxation response from your parasympathetic nervous system (the calming part of your nervous system). Thus, simply taking some time to meditate can result in calmness. Dillbeck and Orme-Johnson gathered thirty-one studies, each of which found meditation to be beneficial for calming down (Dillbeck & Orme-Johnson, 1987).

- Alertness: Meditation enhances your ability to focus. This has been confirmed by fMRI and EEG studies (Hugdahl, 1996).

Affect Regulation Improves with Meditation

Yoga and mindfulness make real and lasting changes in the emotional and thinking centers of the brain. These meditative practices stimulate attentional areas in the frontal lobes, which are key for helping you to think more clearly and make better decisions.

- People who meditated regularly for around 45 minutes a day over a number of years had thicker prefrontal cortices (an area that regulates attentiveness) than nonmeditators of the same age. Furthermore, they found increased thickness of the insular cortex, an area involved in empathy, compassion, fairness, and cooperation. Greater thickness in these areas promotes cognitive and emotional well-being (Lazar et al., 2005). This study showed that the structure of the brain changes in helpful ways following years of meditation practice.

- The cingulate gyrus, where moods and emotions are regulated, is also affected by meditation.

  □ A recent meditation study measured the physiological and brain changes of subjects before, during, and following five days of meditation training. These subjects were compared with a control group who practiced relaxation, but not meditation. The meditation group was better able to regulate their emotional reactions than were those in the control group (Tang et al., 2009).

  □ In a more recent study, this same research group found that structural changes in the brain had occurred from a brief meditation course. They discovered that, in the meditation group, the white matter connectivity increased between the front part of the cingulate gyrus and other structures of the brain (Tang et al., 2010). Thus, meditation was shown to enhance the neural networks that help regulate emotions.

  □ And in their most recent continuation of this work, Tang and Posner (2012) traced out specific white matter increases in the anterior cingulate gyrus from meditation. They showed greater axonal density, which accounts for more interconnections between neurons. They also found expansion of the myelin covering on axons. These changes improved subjects' ability to regulate their emotions.

Different Forms of Meditative Practice Have Different Brain Effects

Each type of meditation has a different effect on how you feel and think. They also have distinct effects on the brain, as measured by EEG, which vary depending on the type of meditation used. Thus, you can pick and choose, to apply the best form of meditation for your purposes.

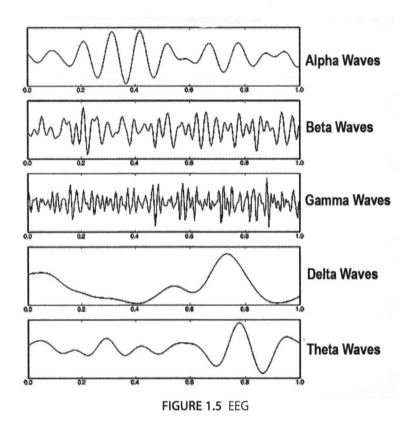

FIGURE 1.5 EEG

- **Focus Meditations:** *Dharana*, postures *(asana)*, and breathing meditations *(pranayama)* are examples of focus meditation where your attention is concentrated on one thing. Subjects doing focus meditation were measured with EEG, and they recorded gamma and beta waves. These short, quick brain waves correlated with deliberately paying attention. Thus, this form of meditation activated the attention centers of the brain. You can learn to direct your thoughts away from disturbing ruminations and toward more positive and hopeful thoughts. Focus meditations, such as concentration on breathing, also bring relaxation and generally reduce stress.

- **Open-Focus Meditations:** Mindfulness and compassion meditations are examples of open-focus meditation. These practices open the focus of your attention. The object of focus is continually changing and moving, moment-by-moment. When the brains of people who practiced open-focus meditation were measured, they showed an increase in theta waves in the frontal and temporal-central areas of the brain, so crucial for regulating emotions. Theta waves correlate with relaxed attention, creativity, tranquility, and restful alertness. Subjects also showed an increase in alpha waves. Alpha waves are associated with relaxed attention. It makes sense to find theta and alpha waves correlated with these nondirected forms of meditation where you are monitoring your ongoing experience in a relaxed, flowing, and open way. You might apply open-focus meditation to help you become more aware and present amid the ever-changing flow of your life.

- **No-Focus Meditations:** Dhyana and Zen are examples of no-focus meditation, characterized by an absence of both focus and effort. As you learn to center in the present moment, free of obstructions from intruding thoughts, you become open to new possibilities. As a result, you can simply respond automatically and effortlessly to stimuli. The EEG associated with no-focus meditation was shown to correlate with a very intense type of alpha wave (Travis and Shear, 2010). These alpha waves are associated with relaxed attention, while the person meditating remains alert with little effort. Increased activity of these waves indicates well-being and comfort. No-focus meditations are helpful for clearing away obstructions and meeting situations with an open mind.

THERAPEUTIC EFFICACY OF YOGA AND MINDFULNESS

Research on yoga and mindfulness has increased exponentially over the past decade. We have outlined a few key studies. Please see our books, *Meditation and Yoga in Psychotherapy* (Simpkins & Simpkins, 2010) and *Zen Meditation in Psychotherapy* (Simpkins & Simpkins, 2011), for further descriptions of the therapeutic efficacy of yoga and mindfulness methods.

Effects of Meditation on Well-being

- Studies of many different forms of meditation have found that the practice improves the quality of life in terms of better memory and productivity, reduced anxiety, improvements in hypertension and sleeplessness, as well as converting loneliness, usually felt as a troubling emotion, into solitude, which can be a source for personal growth and even enlightenment (Dhar, 2002).

- A healthy group of men and women, 18 to 30 years old, participated in a three-month long course in yoga. For 30 days, they practiced yoga breathing exercises. During the last two months, they added a series of yoga postures. Both women and men showed positive improvements and reductions in risk factors for metabolic and cardiovascular diseases, as measured by reduced levels of total cholesterol and triglycerides following the breathing segment of the study. The subjects maintained that improvement when measured following the addition of postures in the third month of the study (Prasad et al., 2006).

- The Transcendental Meditation (TM) project (known as the Maharishi Effect) tested the outcome of meditation on violence and producing a feeling of inner peace and well-being. Four thousand practitioners of TM assembled in Washington, DC, from June 7 to June 30, 1993. The local police monitored the crime rate for the district and found that crimes had decreased 15% during the TM experiment and remained lower for some time after the 21-day event (Hagelin et al., 1999).

Improved Cognitive Capacity

- The ancient yogis believed that yoga techniques combining stimulating postures with calming relaxation meditations would bring about a state of mental balance. Recent studies have found that this claim may be true. The researchers measured the peak latency and peak amplitude of P300 auditory event-related potential (elicited in the decision-making process) in 47 subjects, before and after these combined yoga practices. P300 is an indicator of cognitive processing. The results showed an enhancement of the P300 wave, indicating that the combined practice of stimulating and calming yoga methods improved cognitive functioning (Sarang & Telles, 2006).

Enhanced Compassion

- A recent study found that compassion and altruism can be fostered through meditative training. Following an eight-week training in compassion meditation, participants were invited to participate in an experiment on memory and attention. They entered a waiting room with three chairs, two occupied by confederate experimenters. The subject sat in the empty middle chair. Another experimenter entered on crutches, wearing a boot from an injured foot, groaning in pain. Only 19% of nonmeditating subjects gave up their chairs, whereas 50% of meditators did so. In addition, certain brain areas were correlated with increased altruism: the dorsolateral prefrontal cortex (DLPFC), used for executive control; the inferior parietal cortex for sensing another's suffering and connectivity between the DLPFC; and an area involved in processing reward, the nucleus accumbens for regulating emotion. These activations indicated greater understanding of another's suffering and greater executive and emotional control (Weng et al., 2013).

Enhancements in the Brain Help Combat Psychological Distress

- Mindfulness-based stress reduction (MBSR) programs have proven to be helpful for stress, anxiety, depression, and addiction. But how does mindfulness help? The Hotzel research team, mentioned in the introduction to the research section of this chapter, observed the brain changes in 16 subjects who underwent an eight-week MBSR program compared to 17 subjects in the control group. They found increased gray matter in the cingulate gyrus, the hippocampus, the temporoparietal junction, and the cerebellum. These areas are involved in learning, memory, emotion regulation, and the sense of self (Hotzel et al., 2011).
- Yoga postures were found to increase levels of the neurotransmitter gamma-aminobutyric acid (GABA) in the brain. Eight subjects performed 60 minutes of yoga, compared with 11 control subjects who did a 60-minute reading session. Yoga practitioners had a 27% increase in GABA levels with no change in the group who read. People with depression and anxiety disorders have lower GABA levels, and so yoga may be a helpful addition to their therapy (Streeter et al., 2007).

Stress and Anxiety

- The ability to focus attention, which meditation trains, can improve stress toleration. Vaitl and Ott (2005) found that all altered states involve changes in the focus of attention. These changes can vary from a narrow focus of attention to a broad, extended awareness that includes all in a single grasp. Control of attention span has been shown to have many therapeutic applications: lessening stress is one of them.
- A yoga treatment based on kundalini yoga methods was compared with a stress management program based on cognitive behavioral therapy (CBT). The 33-member subject pool was drawn from a large Swedish company. All subjects were given 10 sessions over a period of four months. The results showed that kundalini yoga was as effective as cognitive behavioral therapy for stress management. All subjects showed significant improvement in psychological effects, such as self-rated stress and stress behavior, anger, exhaustion, and quality of life. Both groups also improved on physiological measures (blood pressure, heart rate, urinary catecholamines, and salivary cortisol). The researchers concluded that like CBT, yoga offers promise as a method for stress reduction (Granath, Ingvarsson, Thiele, & Lundberg, 2006).
- Yoga was used with a group of women who were experiencing anxiety and stress. The subjects underwent a program of postures identified as reducing anxiety and stress by the Iyengar yogic system. The subjects attended two 90-minute sessions per week for eight weeks. When compared with those in the control group, subjects showed significant reductions in anxiety, stress, fatigue, depression, headaches, and back pain along with significant increases in well-being (Michalsen et al., 2005).
- Yoga treatment for veterans who suffered from posttraumatic stress disorder was studied with a group of 62 outpatient veterans, 90% of whom were men. They participated in five, 90-minute sessions given once a week

and were measured pre- and posttreatment. The treatment consisted of one-pointed awareness where each subject focused all his attention on a personally chosen mantra. Following treatment, all subjects showed significant improvement in all outcomes, including anxiety, stress, anger, quality of life, and spiritual well-being, with the largest improvement in anxiety and well-being. The study further found that stronger results were associated with increased frequency of practice (Williams et al., 2005).

Depression

- Mindfulness helps stop overreactions to negative emotions associated with depression and bipolar disorder. But how does that happen? A recent study proposed that mindfulness reduces your self-focus. If you are feeling depressed, you may have an increase in self-focus as you ruminate about yourself and your problems. Depression interferes with a person's ability to reappraise negative emotions. Brain scans show more left hemisphere activation in the language areas and lowered activation in somatosensory areas, such as the parietal lobe, insula, and anterior cingulate, which are involved in the appraisal of emotion (Johnstone et al., 2007; Ressler & Mayberg, 2007).

  Mindfulness subjects expressed feeling sadness, but their brains responded differently. Mindfully attending to the present moment changes neural activity when a person responds to sad stimuli. Activation of the left-hemisphere reappraisal areas of self-focus was lessened in the meditation group, where a shift toward brain areas that correlate with sensory integration occurred. Thus, the researchers concluded that meditators' brains were less involved in self-focus and more engaged in sensing (Farb et al., 2010).

  Meditation offers an alternative to reinterpreting your situation in a more positive way. Instead, you can use other parts of your brain that involve sensory awareness to shift the neural balance and start feeling better. Meditation brings feelings of well-being, which also helps with recovery.

- Several studies have recommended that yoga and mindfulness be added to the treatments for depression. A group of researchers from Brown University reviewed the literature and proposed that these practices offer an attractive alternative for treating depression, because they include some of the active ingredients of treatments that work well for depression: awareness and exercise (Uebelacker et al., 2010).

- A meta-analysis of five studies using different types of yoga interventions for depression examined the severity of the depression, ranging from mild to severe, in yoga practitioners. All five studies found that yoga was helpful and had no adverse effects. One of the studies involving severely depressed subjects showed that rhythmic breathing and relaxation exercises lowered subjects' levels of depression (Khumar, Kaur, & Kaur, 1993).

- Another study gave depressed subjects classes in postures alone and found that the subjects' moods improved as they performed a set of postures (Shapiro, Cook, Davydov, Leuchter, & Abrams 2007).

Substance Abuse

- Mindfulness-based stress reduction programs have been used to help with addiction. One exemplary project taught Vipassana meditation, a form of mindfulness training, to subjects who were in jail. Upon their release, they had a significant reduction in their use of marijuana, crack cocaine, or alcohol as compared to those who had the typical treatments. They also had a decrease of psychiatric symptoms and an increase of an internal locus of control around the substance. In addition, they felt increased optimism (Bowen et. al., 2006).

- Focused meditation has also been shown to help with substance abuse. In an impressively large study of over 1,800 subjects, early researchers in meditation, Herbert Benson and Robert Wallace, showed that a form of focused meditation, Transcendental Meditation, was measurably helpful for overcoming substance abuse (Benson & Wallace, 1972).

- Cravings and impulsivity are two of many difficult challenges that addicts need to overcome. Focused meditation on breathing was shown to increase activity in the prefrontal cortex and particularly in the attention areas of the anterior cingulate cortex. Both parts of the brain are involved in impulse control (Hotzel, 2007). These findings suggest that meditation can play a role in curbing impulses.

CHAPTER 2

Tips for Bringing Yoga and Mindfulness into Your Therapy

The journey of 1000 miles begins with one step.
—Lao-tzu

IN THIS CHAPTER

- Finding tips that will aid you in taking your first steps on the journey to successfully bringing yoga and mindfulness into your practice and your life
  - ☐ How to begin
  - ☐ Where to practice
  - ☐ Timing
  - ☐ Precautions
  - ☐ General advice
- Journaling to start your yoga and mindfulness process

INTRODUCTION

Yoga and mindfulness offer a *way*, a set of practices that you can easily incorporate into your life. When the famous existentialist Jean-Paul Sartre said that existence precedes essence, he meant that what you do and how you live shape what you become. Yoga and mindfulness share in this understanding, and take it one step further, by providing things you can do to foster your well-being. The practices engage your body through postures and breathing and activate your mind through different forms of meditation and mindfulness. As you step on this path and follow the way, you invite your mind-brain-body system into a healthy lifestyle. You literally initiate a process that will rewire your brain, balance your nervous system, clear your thoughts, and calm your emotions.

The tips that follow will answer some of your questions and guide you as you begin. Trust the process and step confidently onto the long-traveled therapeutic path of yoga and mindfulness practice!

The Man Who Finally Found Peace

Ron was a middle-aged man who came to see us for therapy to deal with constant feelings of anxiety. He was one of those tall, barrel-chested men with a commanding personality. Most people would never suspect that he was uncomfortable because he radiated confidence. And yet, therapists with some psychodynamics under their belt would recognize that what he actually felt was quite the opposite. As he confided to us, what he really experienced was insecurity, not confidence. He had achieved acclaim in his career as a researcher at a university, but he never felt satisfied. The more glowing the acclaim he received, the more he felt he needed. He told us, "Perhaps if I could get another award or a better review, I will finally feel okay."

We taught him a yoga and mindfulness meditation. He learned to withdraw his attention from the stream of inner ruminations and create quiet moments. We discussed the idea of craving and how it leads to suffering. As he meditated regularly, he began to realize that he had been caught up in external rewards and had lost his original reason for even becoming a researcher: his love of the truth. He thought about the yamas and niyamas, which helped him to reclaim his ideals. He brought mindfulness to his daily life and was able to direct his efforts away from craving for recognition and toward wholehearted engagement in his research. In quiet meditative moments he became comfortable with who he was, just as he was. By the end of his therapy, Ron had learned that searching outside himself would never stop his anxiety—he had found his peace within.

How To Begin

Tip 1: Learn by doing. Yoga and mindfulness are skills that you practice regularly, so the best way to make them a part of your life is to experience them for yourself. Therefore, don't just read the exercises—do them. The learning takes place through doing it.

Tip 2: Begin with what is easy. Experiment with a wide variety of methods to find which ones feel natural to you. As you do them, you will become aware of your tendencies and talents. Keep in mind that everyone has different tendencies. Try different methods to find which works best for you. You will discover that some of the meditations we offer are easy for you, while others seem difficult. People vary quite a bit in what exercises work for them at first. When we teach yoga and mindfulness in our seminars, we find that typically half of the participants find it easier to be mindful of their body, for example, through breathing or by paying attention to sensations, while the other half find it easier to be mindful of inner experiencing such as visualizing a color or a picture. Later, as you build a skill, you will be able to perform meditations that were initially more difficult for you.

Tip 3: Practice makes perfect. Like learning any new skill, you will improve with practice. You probably can remember when you first learned how to ride a bicycle—you had trouble balancing, and the bike would wobble. But as you practiced more, you discovered a way to ride that allowed the bike to move smoothly and steadily. You gained confidence and a kind of sixth sense. Eventually, you didn't have to think about it; you found yourself just riding. Similarly, with yoga and mindfulness, at first, you make deliberate efforts that may feel awkward and difficult, but eventually you develop instincts for it, and your practice becomes effortlessly centered in the moment.

Tip 4: Start with something concrete. Clearing away thoughts can be difficult to do in the beginning. The monkey mind, as the Buddhists like to call it, just keeps jumping around from thing to thing. You can quiet your monkey mind by focusing on one simple thing, such as posture or breathing. We have found that clients have an easier time when they are given something concrete to do. This focus acts as a springboard to other experiences.

Tip 5: Let new schemas emerge. Look at the squares. As you gaze at them, do you see the squares pointing in one direction? Then, as you shift your attention, can you see the squares switch directions? Both images are there all the time, but your attention tends to look at one or the other. Meditation is like looking at the spaces between, the emptiness that is always there. In fact, in Zen temples, the monks often chant, "Form is emptiness and emptiness is form." This idea is a cornerstone of Zen meditation. In every moment you can shift your gaze from what is to what is not, from activity to nonactivity. And in these quite spaces between, you discover your deeper nature.

WHERE TO PRACTICE

Tip 6. Be comfortable where you are or make it so. The most important consideration in choosing a context for your practice is to feel at ease there. Think of it as a place apart—a sacred space or sanctuary. There are no prerequisite conditions. Consider a place where you feel comfortable, or create one.

Tip 7: Foster the meditation habit with a context. You may think of habits as something negative, behaviors that you want to change or lose, such as smoking or nail-biting. But habits per se are not necessarily negative. Exercise and healthy eating are examples of positive habits. And now, you can cultivate a new healthy habit: meditation.

FIGURE 2.1 Changing Squares

Context can help to reinforce a habit, which is why therapists counsel substance abusers to avoid the places where they typically use drugs or alcohol. You can enlist context to enhance a healthy meditation habit. Return to the same place each time for meditation. Habit and consistency help to set the mood, and like a conditioned response, a meditative response will become easier to bring about.

Tip 8: Make your meditation place simple. The atmosphere of the place for meditation can be very helpful especially when you are first beginning: With experience, you will be able to find inner peace in varied environments. But in the early phases of practice, some settings will prove more conducive to the experience than others. Begin by setting up a peaceful place to meditate. It may be a quiet room or even just a corner in your house or office.

Zen temples tend to have a simple, open space that creates an atmosphere of sanctuary. Traditionally, the walls and floors had very little decoration, except for a single statue or picture that symbolizes meditation. Sometimes a single flower, a simple plant, or a calligraphic scroll is hung on an empty wall. Seating is usually simple, with a cushion placed on the floor. This atmosphere gently invites a meditative experience.

You can create this kind of atmosphere in a corner of your office or home. Make the lighting subdued, not too dark or too bright. Engaging the sense of smell with a subtle incense or fragrant plant may also be helpful. Place a pillow on the floor for sitting and/or a mat to lie down on. Keep decorations simple, but try to add an aesthetic touch to provide a beautiful point of interest.

Tip 9: Meditate in nature. Traditionally, nature has been an inspiration for meditation. Meditation done outdoors, at a park, in the woods, or perhaps in a tranquil garden can help to bring about a feeling of oneness with nature. Water can also have a calming influence. If you have ever listened to the sound of the waves, a bubbling brook, or a waterfall, you have felt water's soothing effects. And water's reflective beauty can captivate your attention.

Tip 10: Meditate in a group. Frequently people find it easier to practice yoga and mindfulness with others. The commitment and momentum of a group practicing together can carry you along. You might like to experience a meditation group at a Buddhist, Daoist, or Yoga center. These institutions offer brief hour-long meditation classes and weekend retreats. Or you might prefer to practice with your family, partner, or friend.

TIMING

Tip 11: Everyone has a minute. We all complain that our lives are so hectic and busy that we could not possibly imagine finding time to practice yoga and mindfulness. But you may be surprised to discover that meditation can be done in as short a period as one minute and still bring positive results. The amount of time to devote to your practice depends on the needs and the situation. Beginners might start with as little as one or two minutes a day. Surely you can spare a minute or two for your own well-being!

Tip 12: Start with what you can manage. If you are suffering from psychological disturbance, begin with a short amount of time for each exercise, even as little as a minute or less. One ADHD businessman jumped from one thing to another. He told us that he had never been able to focus on only one thing, and so he had learned to do three or four things at once. But he felt at a disadvantage when he needed to meet deadlines, and he sincerely wanted to learn how to focus selectively, on one thing at a time. We started him with 10 seconds. This may not seem like much to you, but for him, being able to maintain mindful attention for 10 seconds was a milestone achievement. With practice, he was able to extend the amount of time he focused on each thing he did. Keep in mind that activating inner processing does not rely upon clock time the way conscious cognition does. Sometimes the deepest meditative experience occurs in a flash. Then again, an insight may evolve over many months of practice.

Tip 13: Repeat the exercises often when working on a problem. Practice regularly, at least several times per week. When working on bringing about change, meditate several times each day. Start with a duration of time that you can complete comfortably, even just one minute, but do it several times each day. Regular intermittent practice keeps bringing you back to mindful awareness. We have often found that frequent shorter sessions are easier than trying to maintain one long meditation session. But once again, be willing to individualize your practice to fit your personality, your situation, and your problem.

PRECAUTIONS

Tip 14: Take precautions when performing the body postures. If you are elderly, on medication, or recovering from a medical condition, check with your physician to make sure that yoga and mindfulness practice is safe for you. You may also want to have someone else nearby when you practice the exercises on your own.

Tip 15: Eyes can be opened, closed, or half-open. Eye positions vary with the type of meditation tradition you practice. One way is to keep your eyes fully closed. Sometimes you might prefer to keep your eyes half-open. Another method is to fix your gaze on one point with your eyes open. Experiment with these different ways. We will advise using one method or another at times, but for therapeutic purposes, work with whatever feels most natural for the particular meditation. If you have difficulty focusing, closing your eyes may help to lessen distractions. But if you feel afraid or dizzy when you close your eyes, feel free to keep your eyes half-open or fully open.

GENERAL ADVICE

Tip 16: Commit yourself to the process. As we mentioned in the introduction, yoga and mindfulness doctrine teaches that you can shape your life by what you do and how you live. So, literally doing the exercises, even if you are feeling emotionally uncomfortable, starts a process of change. Both yoga and mindfulness traditions ask practitioners to take a vow that they will be sincerely committed to the process. Taking a vow helps give direction and purpose to the journey.

Make a vow now, a promise, that you will do some yoga and mindfulness practice each day, even if for only for a minute or two at a time. Make your vow doable for you, but be sincere in your efforts. You may not feel like practicing every time you make the effort, and that is to be expected. Don't chastise yourself if you have trouble sometimes. Remember that you are walking a path. Sometimes the terrain is smooth and sometimes it may be rocky. But as you travel along, you will learn more about traveling itself, and the journey will become easier. Keep your faith in yourself and in the process, and you will succeed. "If a snail sets out for Mount Fuji, surely he will get there" (ancient Japanese proverb).

Tip 17: Remember to take an inward glance regularly! With your sincerity as a resource, take your first steps on the path. This involves remembering to practice, not just during your session or present time, but also at random times during your daily routine. You may be pleasantly surprised how your yoga and mindfulness deepens and grows.

JOURNALING

We encourage you to keep a journal as you go through this workbook. Keeping a journal will add another dimension to your awareness, which is always helpful! Reflect on these questions in your journal:

1. How do you usually begin something new? Consider how to use your typical way to help you implement yoga and mindfulness into your life.

2. Can you approach this new venture with an open mind?

3. What are your hopes for integrating these practices into your life?

4. If you are new to yoga and mindfulness, what do you think is reasonable to expect from it? Now that you have been given an introduction, what do you think it will probably be like?

5. If you already practice yoga and/or mindfulness, note some of your experiences. What have you learned about yourself from the practices?

6. Take a moment to sit quietly, and then record your experience.

CHAPTER 3

Warming Up by Honing Your Meditation Tools

The craftsman who would perfect his work must first sharpen his tools.

—Confucius

IN THIS CHAPTER

- Learn tools to enhance your yoga and mindfulness practice
- Follow easy-to-do exercises to build on the skills you already have that help you flow naturally into yoga and mindfulness practices
- Hone your sensory tools, attention tools, and body awareness tools
- Have a vivid experience of how the mind and body are connected through the ideomotor effect
- Begin journaling to add feedback to your experiences and prepare for the next steps

INTRODUCTION

Whenever you go about doing something, you inevitably use tools. Tools work best when you use the *right* tool for the job—a screwdriver for a screw and a hammer for a nail. And you want your tools to be in good condition. For example, when slicing tomatoes, you need a particularly sharp, serrated knife.

Although you might not give it much thought, you use psychological tools all the time, including sensory tools, attention tools, and body awareness tools. You can develop and hone these tools to facilitate your yoga and mindfulness practice. The exercises in this chapter guide you in developing these tools to enhance your practice of yoga and mindfulness.

Perhaps you doubt that you can succeed in something that requires focus and discipline such as meditation, especially if you are having problems. But, honing your tools will bring you confidence. You can be reassured that the therapeutic application of yoga and mindfulness starts with the tools you already have and builds on them, step-by-step. Training to improve your skill with your tools can have a broader positive effect on your therapy, as well as enhancing your general adjustment to challenges.

The learning is experiential, so it is important that you do the exercises. You should be able to find some time to fit them in, since they only take a few minutes each. Repeat the exercises at different times and in different places if possible. You can also complete these exercises between sessions as "homework." We encourage you to hone your yoga and mindfulness tools because skills improve with practice!

The Man Who Reversed the Hands of Time

Joe was a long-time methamphetamine user. You may have heard the expression that there are no old addicts, and Joe was a good illustration. Even though he was only 30 years old, he appeared deathly thin and frail. His family doctor told him he had the heart of a 70-year-old man. He recounted the doctor's warning: "If you don't stop whatever you are doing right now, you will die, and soon!" Joe went on to complain, "I don't want to die, but I don't know how to live without drugs!" He believed that methamphetamine made him feel good and work better. Without it, life was empty and boring, and he was slow in performing important work-related actions. But he knew he had to find another way, or his life would end.

We encouraged him to meditate, beginning with focusing on his sensory experience. He began to notice what was happening in his body, and he realized that the drugs he used did not make him feel as good as he had thought. He felt his heart race. He noticed that his attention jumped around. And he realized that when he was high, he was completely out of control. He recognized that he was not actually performing actions faster; he just thought that he was. And he was less efficient. He became painfully aware of all the ways that methamphetamine was hurting him. His motivation to stop grew stronger.

As he gained skills in meditation, he practiced holding his attention on an object of focus: his emotions. He began feeling more in control and noticed that he genuinely felt good when he was with people. He also began to note better qualities emerging from within. He became more comfortable with himself and expressed his natural personality. Eventually, he decided to look for work in a people-oriented field, where speed of action was not the main concern, his better qualities were.

He continued to incorporate regular meditation into his daily routine. As he used drugs less, he began to feel better. Eventually, he completely withdrew from drugs under the close supervision of his doctor. He truly reversed the hands of time, as his heart returned to functioning like the heart of a normal 30-year-old man. He had found a better source of excitement and happiness in the world of people and events, accomplishing goals without speeding.

Sensory Tools

Your sensory system can attune you to the world. You can sharpen your senses so that each one becomes a gateway to clearer perception. Practice the following exercise several times throughout your day or evening. As your skills build, your sensory awareness will be enhanced.

Sensing Temperature

Begin by closing your eyes and make note of the temperature in your right palm by touching the palm of your right hand to your upper left arm. If you are wearing long sleeves, roll up your sleeve so that your palm touches your skin directly. Take a moment to notice how warm or cool your palm feels in comparison to your arm.

Now, touch a table or chair. How does your palm's temperature feel? Is it warmer or cooler than before? Give yourself a minute or two to sense the temperature. Next, place your palm on your clothes at your shoulder, paying close attention to the temperature of your palm as you do so. Then, touch a cool glass of water, or perhaps the inside of your refrigerator. Note the temperature of your palm now as you are placing it on a cool object. Finally, hold your palm out, palm up, and feel the temperature without touching anything. You will notice how your sensation of temperature is closely related to the context.

Repeat this experiment, but turn your attention to the textures of the things you are touching. So, as you touch your skin, notice the surface as you touch it. You will feel a distinct difference between the texture of your skin, your clothing, a cool glass, or simply holding your palm up in the air.

Sensing Sound: Listening as You Speak

You are always talking, but how often do you really listen to the sound of your voice as you speak? Although you might feel silly if you are sitting by yourself, begin speaking. Just say whatever comes to mind for 30 seconds or so, but as you do, listen! Hear the sound of your voice: listen to the tones, the pauses, and the cadence.

Next, close your eyes and speak again, listening to the sound of your voice once more. Do you find it easier or more difficult to hear with your eyes closed? Your answer to this question will give you some clues for how to easily find your way into meditation. We all have our natural tendencies, and it is helpful to know yours to help you discover your best pathway into the experience.

Finally, cover your ears and speak again. You may notice that you hear your own voice clearly, but any outside sounds disappear. Listen for a minute or so and notice what you hear. Then uncover your ears and compare as you speak again.

Sense of Touch: Sensing an Object

You can also use any of your other senses, like your sense of touch, to help you develop your meditation tools. Clients who have difficulty focusing attention will often find it easier to focus on something specific, such as an object. In the next exercise, you can experiment focusing your attention on sensations by using a small stone that you find outside. This exercise can help to enhance body awareness and the ability to become aware of sensations.

Using Touch as a Meditative Tool

Find a small stone that interests you. It could be rough or smooth, brightly colored or dull, anything you find visually interesting. Pick one that is a few inches in diameter so that it has a little bit of weight to it. You can also do this exercise with any everyday object such as a cell phone, a pen, or a wallet,

Hold one hand out in front of you, palm facing up, and place your stone in the palm of your hand. Focus all your attention on the sensation you feel with the stone on your hand. Can you feel how heavy it is? Is it warmer or cooler than your skin? Can you feel the texture of the stone? Keep your attention focused on the sensations.

Next, remove the stone from your palm, but keep noticing the sensations in your palm. How do these sensations compare with how you felt when the stone was there? Notice the temperature, the air on your skin, or anything else that you perceive.

Place the object back in your palm and experience it there once again, noticing all the sensations.

Hold both of your hands in front of you, palms up, and compare them. You will notice interesting differences. And finally, remove the stone from your hand and pay attention to both palms. You will probably find it easier to notice your sensations now that you have done these exercises.

For a variation, lie down on your back, close your eyes, and place the stone on your stomach. Move the stone around, to your arm or leg, and repeat the exercise. Then, take the stone away and pay attention to those areas, noticing the difference.

Sense of Vision: Working with the Tools of Seeing

Seeing is an important component of yoga and mindfulness, but people are not often unified with their experiences. For example, while you are looking at one thing, you might be thinking about something else. You are always looking. In fact, the visual system of the brain is highly developed, and humans rely on vision a great deal for orienting to the world. But, how often do you take time to see? The exercises in this section develop your visual sensing, beginning with relaxing your eyes to help you see better and more fully.

We make great demands on our eyes in both work and recreation, particularly with all the time we spend at our computers and electronic devices. Rarely do we think about our eyes unless they become a problem to us; however, eyes, like other parts of the body, can be relaxed and freed from rigid patterns. Viable methods for training and improving vision were developed and used in yoga and later rediscovered in other systems. Here we include some exercises that will help your eyes to relax and see better in preparation for the next series of exercises.

Eye Swings

Stand comfortably, weight balanced evenly between your two feet with your arms at your sides. Begin to swing your arms around from one side of your body to the other. Allow your body to twist with your arms, pivoting your feet as well. Let your head turn along with your body. As you make each swing, keep your eyes straight ahead and relaxed, so that your field of vision moves as you move. Your surroundings will seem to rush past you. Do not stop your head from flowing with the movement. After several minutes of pivots, back and forth, your eyes will feel looser.

Eye Palming

Your eyes can become very tired, and this tension carries through your whole body. Palming can relieve and relax your eyes. Sit or lie down comfortably. Close your eyes. Place your palms very lightly over your eyelids. Your fingertips can rest on the top of your forehead. Do not press. Rest for several minutes. Allow your eyes to relax beneath your palms. Let go of any unnecessary tension you might notice in your face.

ATTENTION TOOLS

Information Box: What Is Focus, What Is Attention?

1. Attention engages many parts of the brain working together in an activated, dynamic unity.

2. What is sensed interacts with what is thought through attention.

3. Focus is the selecting mechanism through which attention is directed, creating the synthesis of perception.

Yoga and mindfulness provide many methods for sharpening attention, as you will see in later chapters. These attention exercises will build skills that will enhance your yoga and mindfulness practice.

Directing Attention

This exercise develops your ability to focus your attention carefully so that you can perceive something you see clearly and completely. Figure 3.1 provides a picture for you to look at, and use it if you find it interesting; however, this exercise works best when the person is interested. So, if you do this exercise in your office, you might have a prized picture on your wall and can direct your attention there. A teenager might find her iPod a more fascinating object of focus. Use whatever is of most interest, and you will find this exercise easier to do.

FIGURE 3.1 Meditation Picture

Looking and Sensing

Look at a picture or object. Notice the shapes, the textures, and the light and dark parts. Notice everything you can about the picture. When you have a good sense of the picture, close your eyes and imagine it within. As you imagine the picture or object, do you have any gaps? If so, open your eyes to look again. Notice things you might have missed the first time. When you feel ready, close your eyes again. Continue to open and close your eyes until you have a clear inner sense of the picture.

As an alternative, look at the small stone that you used in the sensing exercise. Set it down in front of you and sit down. Look at the stone for several minutes. Notice everything you can about it: shape, color, texture, size, how the light affects it, and anything else that you see. Keep your attention on this object. If your mind wanders to something else, bring it back. After a few minutes, move on to the next exercise.

Inner Attention Exercise

The skills you developed in sensing can also help you focus your attention inwardly. The exercise that follows helps you connect the outer world of experience to the inner world of experience. This exercise involves focus of inner attention. Do this immediately after the sensing exercise with the stone (or other object of your choice).

Inner Focus I

Sit comfortably and close your eyes. Recall the stone. Think about what you noticed when the stone was resting in your palm. The image might be vivid or vague. What is most important is that you concentrate on it. Keep focused for at least several minutes. Bring your attention back to the experience if you find your mind wandering.

Recognizing Inner Visualizing

Some people have trouble visualizing and feel that the previous exercise is difficult to do. Although you may lack the ability, it's also possible that you just don't know how to recognize it when it happens. This exercise is based on how the perceptual system works, where certain neurons become fatigued when presented with a stimulus, thereby allowing the others to appear. After performing this exercise, you may find it easier to visualize.

Inner Focus II

Tape a red square, around 5 inches tall and 7 inches wide on a white wall, or create a red square of that size against a white background on your computer screen.

When you have the red square within clear view, look at it for several minutes without looking away. Just look at the red color. Trace the edges with your eyes, keeping your attention fully focused on the red. Then, close your eyes and wait. Do you see a green square emerge? Most people will, unless they are color-blind. If you are color-blind, you might see a different color or a grayscale square emerge. This afterimage is similar to visualizing. Once you have experienced it, other kinds of formerly unrecognized visualizations will become easier to recognize. This is a sensitizing percept—opening your mind to a possibility that is already there but not noticed.

Opening Attention

Look at your stone again, but this time, let your attention wander. So, if it reminds you of something else in the room that catches your eye, look there. Let your attention wander to wherever it is drawn, looking all around.

Next, close your eyes and think about the stone for a moment. Then, let your thoughts associate with whatever occurs to you. Allow your attention to move along to anything that you are interested in thinking about. Just keep your attention moving and flowing spontaneously. Do this for several minutes, until you feel ready to stop.

BODY TOOLS

Your body is intimately integrated with your nervous system. And the activity of the nervous system correlates with what you think and feel. Herein lies the power of yoga and mindfulness: by linking your attention to your body, you can shift difficult psychological problems in a more positive direction. This section shows you how your mind and body are linked together and then gives simple exercises to begin working with your awareness of your body experience.

Mind-Body Link

There is a link between mind and body, known as the ideomotor link, where an idea held in the mind is translated automatically into a bodily response. When you look at how brain areas are located, you see that the motor strip on the cortex is situated right next to the sensory strip behind it and the thinking prefrontal cortex in front of it. The ideomotor effect proceeds from having an idea or sensory experience that is translated into a bodily response.

Begin by experiencing this fascinating ideomotor effect, and later learn how to use it to enhance your yoga and mindfulness practice.

Ideomotor Effect I

To experience the ideomotor effect, close your eyes and imagine a tart lemon. Think about the yellow pulp, the lemony aroma, and the tart taste. Then imagine popping a slice of lemon into your mouth. Taste the tart flavor. Bite down to release the lemony juice. Give yourself time to have a reaction. Be sensitive and aware of subtle responses. Does your mouth begin to water? If so, you have experienced the ideomotor effect: a reaction to an imagined image becomes directly expressed in your bodily response.

Some people may find that the response is immediate and very distinct, while others may not have as dramatic and bold a reaction. Even a tiny sensation can be nurtured into a very useful skill to be applied when you need it, so accept whatever occurs, with the understanding that you will be developing new skills as you continue reading.

Traditional Ideomotor Exercise

This exercise uses the imagination of movement, which is translated into real movement in your hand. The famous French chemist Michel-Eugène Chevreul (1786–1889) is credited with first creating this device for experiencing the ideomotor effect, known as the Chevreul Pendulum.

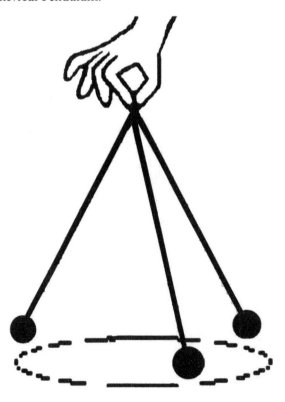

FIGURE 3.2 Ideomotor

Ideomotor Effect II

Get a plumb bob, ring, or any small, heavy object. Attach it to a string. Hold the string from the top and let the object dangle freely. Keep your arm comfortably extended, with your elbow bent slightly. Now close your eyes. Imagine that the pendulum begins to swing back and forth. Picture it vividly in your mind. Do not deliberately move or interfere with the hand that holds the string. Instead, focus on the image of swinging. Visualize the rhythmic sweep of the swing becoming longer, back and forth. After a few minutes, open your eyes and look at the pendulum. Most people will find that it is swinging back and forth, just as they had imagined.

Close your eyes again. Imagine that the object begins to swing in the other direction. Exaggerate the image so that the arc becomes larger and larger in the new direction. Picture it as vividly as possible. Once again, do not disturb the hand that holds the string. Simply focus on your visualization. After a minute or so, open your eyes. Is the pendulum swinging in the new direction?

Close your eyes one last time. Imagine that the pendulum swings in a circle. Allow the circular orbit to become larger and larger. Open your eyes to check, and you will likely see the pendulum moving in a circle.

Some people can do this almost immediately. Others will expand their abilities over time. Practice will enhance the effect.

JOURNALING

Record your responses to each exercise in this way:

Before: What do you experience right before you begin an exercise? Note what is happening for you right before.

During: Notice any thoughts, feelings, or sensations as you do the exercise.

After: Write down your reflections after each exercise.

CHARTING

Record for one week what you do each day, and note what you think and/or feel as you are doing it. Approach the chart as a scientist—recording data objectively.

FIGURE 3.3 One Week Warm-up: Doing, Thinking, Feeling

	What are you doing?	What are you thinking?	What are you feeling?
Monday morning midday evening			
Tuesday morning midday evening			
Wednesday morning midday evening			
Thursday morning midday evening			

(Continued)

FIGURE 3.3 *(Continued)*

	What are you doing?	What are you thinking?	What are you feeling?
Friday morning midday evening			
Saturday morning midday evening			
Sunday morning midday evening			

Part II

The Practices

*When you do something, if you fix your mind on the activity with some confidence, the
quality of your state of mind is the activity itself.*
—Shunryu Suzuki, 1979

IN PART II

- Exercises for practice from the Eight Limbs
  - Yamas and niyamas (dos and don'ts)
  - Asanas (postures)
  - Pranayama (breathing)
  - Pratyahara (withdrawal)
  - Dharana (focus)
  - Dhyana (opening)
  - Mindfulness (awareness)
- Case examples to illustrate the use of these practices in therapy

Yoga and mindfulness provide a system of practices, which are things to do that lead you to a more awake, alert consciousness. The key is in *doing*. As you *do* the practices, you put yourself on a path that leads you to a new place: greater awareness with a unified mind, body, and spirit. At first, you must make deliberate efforts, but as you gain some mastery with the practices of yoga and mindfulness, fuller awareness emerges with spontaneous ease.

The Eight Limbs of yoga are the classic steps to follow for making this transformation. The varied practices teach a different skill, including how to raise your motivation and solidify your intent, breathing meditations to regulate and help you become conscious of breathing, body positioning that is relaxed and alert, and different ways to focus your attention. Mindfulness provides a method for increasing awareness in your everyday life. Taken together, these practices awaken your consciousness for healthy changes in thought, emotion, and behavior. The techniques taught in Part II form the basis for the therapeutic applications in Part III. So, practice them as each chapter unfolds and enjoy, as you become more proficient!

CHAPTER 4

Using the Dos and Don'ts (Yamas and Niyamas) for Cognitive Reframing and Healthy Habits

Each of us literally chooses, by his ways of attending to things,
what sort of a universe he shall appear to himself to inhabit.
—William James, 1896

IN THIS CHAPTER

- Learn about the yoga yamas, what you should not do, and niyamas, what you should do
- Use the yamas and niyamas to strengthen and clarify your motivation
- Record your reflections about each yama and niyama to gather your intention and inspire your actions in helpful directions
- Practice a meditation associated with each yama and niyama to help initiate a process for actualizing your intentions

INTRODUCTION

According to yoga and mindfulness philosophy, you can make a difference by what you do and how you live. The first two limbs on the yoga tree of practices are the yamas and niyamas, things you should and things you should not do. These dos and don'ts help you shape your destiny in a positive direction. They can serve as sounding boards to resonate with your motivations and intentions.

If you have ever made a New Year's resolution that you didn't keep, you know that it's not always possible to stop a bad habit by just deciding to. You may need to do, deeper psychological work to make it happen. Making a sincere decision to change and setting your intention in the right direction will help. Building strong intention unites your conscious and unconscious mind to see your decision through. The yamas and niyamas act as stimuli for your journey, unifying your intention with your mind, body, and spirit, toward a healthier, wiser you.

The Woman Who Found the Courage to Seek Higher Values

All people make mistakes, but having the humility to admit fault and correct the action may be painful. The yamas and niyamas offer a framework to help you come to terms with wrongdoing and forge a healthier, happier direction.

Sharon was a heroin addict who began therapy to give up drugs. Even though she had deep, dark circles under her eyes, she was slim and attractive, with angular features and an intense expression. She had led her life on the edge, doing petty crimes and prostitution to support her habit. Her parents had served time in jail, and she saw no better future for herself. From all that she had done and been, she doubted her personal integrity. But we saw her potential. She needed to develop the strength and honor to actualize it. Through yoga and mindfulness therapy, she began to feel strong enough to withdraw completely from drugs. Upon our recommendation, she checked into a hospital to withdraw safely. But once she was out again, she asked us, "How can I find the strength to stay sober and resist the pull of *the life* [of crime and drugs]? I don't know how to do anything else!"

We taught her about the yamas and niyamas. She went through each one, and cultivated a strong resolve, using the exercises described in this chapter. Because of this work, she gained the ability to detach herself from harmful influences. As she thought about the last two niyamas, she considered something she had never thought possible: higher goals for herself. She began to think beyond just getting by and dared, instead, to search for what was meaningful over what was just pragmatic or clever. She had always considered herself a daring person, and liked the idea of taking a risk. She went to community college even though she felt out of place. Much to her surprise, she discovered that she really loved art. And her teachers saw that she had artistic talent. In time, she found honest work as a sales clerk at an arts supply store to support herself while she was in school. She began to develop her style as a painter and eventually found patrons who believed in the depth and sensitivity of her work. Years after stopping therapy, she contacted us to tell us she was happily married to an honest man who had never engaged in crime. They had two children, and now that both were in school, she was devoting much of her time to painting and teaching art to children.

THE YAMAS

The word *yama* means restraint, self-control, and discipline. The yamas are what you should not do and are also often referred to as the abstinences. They include:

1. *Ahimsa*, not harming self or others
2. *Satya*, not lying
3. *Asteya*, not stealing
4. *Bramacharya*, control, moderation and restraint
5. *Aparigraha*, nonattachment

Ahimsa, Not Harming Self or Others

Not to harm makes a great deal of sense, but if you are having psychological problems, you might inadvertently be harming yourself or others, physically, emotionally, or financially. But what is the source of harm? Often it comes from a feeling of lacking within. To truly do no harm requires self-confidence, so that you don't feel a need to be defensive or lash out. Hostility often derives from insecurity or internalized anger. With ahimsa in mind, you will find it easier to resolve inner turmoil and put the brakes on harming behavior. You can even begin extending compassion toward others and toward yourself.

1. *Buddha believed that the first step on the path to end suffering is to face that you are suffering. Thus, begin now by noticing any ways that you might be causing harm to others or to yourself and write down how you may be causing suffering to yourself and others.*

   Try to be objective, but don't be too harsh on yourself. Even if you have been engaged in actions that you believe to be destructive, you are taking constructive steps now. You can trust that the steps along the yoga and mindfulness path offer forgiveness and the means to make amends.

2. *Write down how you might be able to do the opposite of harming: do no harm or even to show compassion to yourself and others. How can you help others? And equally important, how can you help yourself?*

Ahimsa Meditation

Did you ever hear of the old adage, look before you leap? When pulled by strong emotion that might lead you into hostile action, take a meditative moment to look within. Stop, even sit down, and focus on breathing. At first, your breathing might seem labored. You might feel warmth in your face or shaking in your body. But just notice, sit quietly, even count your breaths. Accept whatever you are feeling and keep noticing your breathing. You will learn more about breathing meditations in Chapter 5. Please feel free to use this or any of the other meditations in this book to help you stop and take an inward look before you leap into ways that harm yourself or others.

Satya, Not Lying

Satya, the second yama, means to abstain from falsehood. This means to seek truth, to speak the truth, and to be truthful in what you do. Psychological problems often involve self-deception or deception of others, a kind of lying. In a very deep sense, all psychotherapy seeks inner and outer truth, through living in congruence with your true self, as well as living honestly with others. Being sincere in thought and deed, many of your problems dissolve. And as you live honestly in accord with who you are and what you truly believe, inner intention unifies with outer action, and so discord dissolves, leading to healthier living.

1. *Write down any ways that you may be lying to others. Do you speak truthfully or do you tend to bend the truth or express a partial truth?*

2. *Record how you are deceiving yourself. Are you making excuses or perhaps expecting more than is realistically possible, and then getting angry with yourself?*

3. *Are you true to who you are within—your true self—when you act? Or are you deceiving yourself by trying to please others or live up to a standard that doesn't feel right for you? By putting these thoughts on paper, you will find it easier to sort out what is right for you, and eventually find ways to live truthfully in thought, word, and deed.*

Satya Meditation

Truth begins with awareness. Sit quietly and take an inward glance. Notice what you are experiencing right now. Stay with the present moment, sensing and noticing whatever is there. If your mind jumps to the past or future, gently bring it back as soon as you notice. Take an inward glance whenever you feel yourself straying from the truth. In the moment of awareness, you will feel less pulled to lie or deceive.

Asteya, Not Stealing

Asteya, the third yama, means to abstain from stealing. Stealing is not just theft of property; it can be interpreted more broadly. For example, stealing doesn't have to be limited to taking something that isn't yours; it may also apply to *desiring* to have something that isn't yours, such as having someone else's relationships or another's success. But it can also refer to taking on responsibility for another's burdens. By recognizing what is and is not truly yours, you open the way to realize the potential that is rightfully yours, no more and no less.

1. *Write down any ways that you might want to have something or someone that is not yours.*

☐ *Do you feel unhappy if someone else has something that you would like to have? Do you feel envious, angry, or hurt?*

2. *Do you take on other people's emotions, blame, or anger, as your own?*

3. *Now, return to your true self. Think about who you truly are and what is yours. List the things that you can be grateful for having.*

☐ *Consider those things that you own that you appreciate having.*

☐ *Think of the qualities about yourself, personality traits, even quirks that are uniquely you. Even though you may not typically consider them assets, feel grateful for these things, since they reflect your deeper nature.*

☐ *Begin considering ways to develop your qualities into strengths. For example, a client of ours who complained of being stubborn turned it into determination and strong will. A forgetful client learned to forget her bad habits. Think of how you can turn a seemingly negative trait into a positive asset.*

Asteya Meditation

Feel gratitude for all that you have, including the things you own and value, people who matter to you, as well as your positive qualities: your skills, talents, and potential. Consider all the abundance in your life and be grateful.

Bramacharya, Control, Moderation, and Restraint

Bramacharya, control, moderation, and restraint, is another yama that can be interpreted in many ways. For the purposes of your self-transformation, it involves not engaging in excess so that you can have more energy for higher purposes. The word *brama* means divine consciousness, and *charya* derives from the root word *car*, meaning to move. So, *bramacharya* implies moving or living with a higher consciousness. The yogis of the past practiced chastity as a means to free their energy for spiritual devotion to Brahman, God, but a modern interpretation means to avoid overindulging your senses so that you can be free to cultivate higher consciousness.

1. *Have you been subscribing to the idea that more is better, without realizing it? If you struggle with overeating, too much partying, substance abuse, or any other excess, you may be overvaluing your sensory experience. Record your thoughts.*

2. *Seek the higher value in things and in yourself. If you were not hampered by your problems, what would you most like to do with your life? What do you value?*

Bramacharya Meditation

Sit quietly for a few moments outdoors. If you can, visit a park, garden, beach, or lake, or even sit near a flower or a tree. Take a few minutes to look around and notice the beauty of nature. But, if going outdoors is impossible right now, study nature nearby. You can look up at the sky through the window or observe a houseplant. Let yourself marvel at the magnitude of the world around you or the intricate beauty in a single leaf. The ineffable, spiritual quality of life is always there around you, so take a moment, here and there, to notice it. Enjoy it now and let yourself feel inspired.

Aparigraha, Nonattachment

Aparigraha, the fifth yama, teaches you to avoid grasping, and instead to cultivate detachment. The idea is not that you must renounce all possessions, but rather not to *need* them to ensure your happiness. Ultimately, aparigraha suggests that all the things you cling to, material objects, such as old clothes you haven't worn for years and deep emotional hurts and annoyances from the past, hold you back from a clear and open future. By being nonattached, you are free to be open and accepting of your deeper nature.

1. *What is the source of your happiness?*
2. *Do you believe that your material possessions bring you happiness? If so, consider how you have bestowed these things with that meaning.*
3. *Will having more things make you happier? Consider the ways that you are endowing this material possession with power over your happiness. If you give it power, you can also choose not to.*
4. *Explore the idea that the real source of happiness is found within.*
5. *Consider past hurts and wrongs that still haunt you. Think of how these past wrongs hold you back now. Can you let them go?*
6. *Write down your thoughts about grasping and letting go.*

Aparigraha Meditation

Sit quietly, breathe comfortably, and focus as you exhale. With each exhale, visualize release, letting go of tension and worry. Think of aparigraha, nonpossessiveness, as you release. Practice this meditation when you feel yourself grasping for control. Enjoy a moment of freedom.

THE NIYAMAS

The niyamas are those things that you should do, also known as the observances. There are five niyamas:

1. *Shaucha*, purity
2. *Santosha*, contentment
3. *Tapas*, austerity
4. *Pranitara*, attentiveness to self-study, great literature, and inner reflection on matters of meaningful spirituality
5. *Ishvara pranidana*, devotion to higher value, whether God or perhaps, an organizing spiritual principle

Shaucha, Purity

Shaucha is the practice of purity. Your body is the vehicle to higher consciousness, and so it makes sense to keep that vehicle pure and receptive. Shaucha literally refers to hygiene, keeping your body clean, well groomed, and well cared for, and in good physical shape. Yoga was one of the early proponents of natural foods and encourages following a healthy diet to keep your internal organs well nourished. But shaucha can also be interpreted as purity and refinement of thought and speech, using such practices as clearing your mind through meditation or focusing on the breath.

Purity has a feedforward-feedback effect. As you adopt the practice of wholesome habits, the practice feeds back as you become healthier, which in turn feeds forward to a healthier mind, body, and spirit.

1. *Review your daily hygiene habits. Write down your routines for cleanliness and care of your body (e.g., daily routines, dentists, doctors)*

2. *Review your diet. Do you include fresh fruits and vegetables every day? Do you drink several glasses of fresh water? Think about the different food groups and ensure that you eat a balanced diet. If not, how can you alter your diet to become healthier?*

3. *Add regular exercise to your routine. The practice of pranayama breathing with asana postures offers a good way to get in shape. If you are completely inactive, adding a short walk each day will get you started well. We recommend that you check with your medical doctor to ensure that you have no physical conditions that prevent you from a moderate exercise routine. Set a reasonable goal that you can easily do, and then stick to it.*

4. *Make note of your thoughts. Do you find your mind filled with negative, disturbing thoughts? If so, begin by recognizing that you are doing so, and commit yourself to the process of purifying your thoughts. This may involve working through conflicts to bring you to a point of forgiveness and compassion. But for now, begin by accepting that you have such thoughts, commit yourself to the process, and have faith that you will be making changes.*

Shaucha Meditation to a Clear Mind

This exercise incorporates peaceful visualization to slow down your mental chatter. Although we describe a scene in nature, feel free to use any peaceful place you prefer that is personally meaningful to you.

Sit quietly with your eyes closed. Imagine sitting on the shore of a pond. The pond is alive with activity. Frogs croak; crickets sing; birds fly overhead; a fish jumps out of the water, feeding on insects, splashes back, and jumps again after a bit, in another spot. Wind whips over the water, stirring up the muddy bottom. All is movement. Then gradually, as the day passes, the conditions begin to shift. The wind dies down. The frogs settle in for a nap, the crickets are silent, the birds perch in the trees, the fish stops jumping and waits. The pond is quiet. The murky rippled surface calms as the mud sinks. Now, all is stillness. Imagine this scene vividly. Stay with the quiet, clear water.

Santosha, Contentment

Santosha is being content and happy with what you have. It is an active process. Choose to be happy. Don't wait for happiness to happen to you.

You might tend to overlook the positive aspects of your life, but you can deliberately choose to appreciate what you have, and recognize the good in things as they are: the beautiful sky overhead, the comfortable chair that you sit in, the help others give you. Santosha encourages you to appreciate what you have in your life, just as it is. And acceptance should extend to other people, not just yourself.

Santosha is easy when things are going well. But if something bad happens, it can be challenging to maintain your contentment. Even in the midst of psychological problems or negative circumstances, you can find happiness. By cultivating the ability to face things as they are, you can find some contentment wherever you find yourself. Contentment with what is can do much to relieve your suffering and set yourself on a path to healing.

1. *List some things that you can feel happy about. If you are feeling depressed, this might seem like an impossible request, but look carefully. It can be as subtle as a bird that flies by in the sky or a smile from a stranger as you walk down the street.*

2. *Can you think of ways you can bring contentment to others in your life? Sometimes we spend time talking about how awful things are, but you are just as free to discuss the positive aspects that may be overlooked. Consider this possibility now.*

3. *Do you complain of feeling out of control with the circumstances in your life? This may be so, but something is in your control. Think of it in another way: You may not have chosen your life circumstance, but you always have a choice with regard to how to react to your life circumstance. Experiment now by taking a more positive, hopeful attitude to it, no matter how bad it seems to be. Instead, consider the situation as a challenge to rise to.*

Santosha Meditation

Next time you are facing something you resent but have to endure, such as being at a standstill in heavy traffic or feeling angry with someone close to you, try thinking of something to appreciate, and learn from the situation. Is there anything you can find? For example, while you are stuck in traffic, can you appreciate the moment while you reflect and look around? Ill-mannered drivers give you the opportunity to practice good manners, considerateness, and correct driving skills. Or is there something you appreciate about the person who angers you? Any moment offers an opportunity to be your personal best, and express wholesome values in action. Can you imagine saying something positive or helpful to that person? Do this meditation in varied uncomfortable situations. You may be surprised to find that you can be more content than you think!

Tapas, Austerity

Tapas, or austerity, involves building your capacity to handle adversity, a kind of toughening of the spirit. Having a healthy lifestyle will make you stronger physically, but mental toughness is something that you can cultivate. Tapas of the mind means developing your ability to influence thinking, regulate emotions, and keep your mind steady when you want to. All the yoga practices help to carry out tapas in everyday life, as the later chapters will teach.

1. *To begin, commit yourself to becoming stronger. Note down some ways that you can take a stronger attitude. Do you tend to say things like, "I can't stand it." Or "Why does this happen to me?"*
2. *Write down some alternative ways to think about it, such as "I know this is difficult, but I can handle it." Or, "Better that it happens to me than to someone who is in a worse situation." Experiment now with changing some of the ways you tend to interpret circumstances as terrible and reframe them into positive statements.*

Tapas Meditation

Do you feel like a slave to temperature? Are you terribly uncomfortable if the weather is too hot or too cold? The Tibetan monks have shown us that human beings have the capacity to alter their skin temperature at will, using meditation. They test their skill in body warming by drying a wet cloth on their bare back in freezing temperatures. You can build your tolerance of temperature extremes by practicing this meditation on hand warming. We encourage you to have confidence. We have taught this exercise to thousands of people, including children who especially enjoy mastering this skill!

Place the palm of your right hand on your left upper arm and notice the temperature of your hand. This gives you a baseline temperature for where you are starting. Then, place the palms of your hands together and vividly imagine them getting warmer. You might think of a warm day, imagine holding your hands in front of a fireplace, or simply visualize the warmth between your palms increasing. Hold your palms together in this way for several minutes. Then, test your palm again against your upper arm, and if you have been successful, your palm will be warmer. You can use this skill next time you find yourself feeling too cold.
As a more advanced application, hold your palms facing each other, but keep them several inches apart.

Svadhyaya, Self-Education

Svadhyaya means self-study and involves cultivating a self-reflective consciousness. In a sense, psychotherapy is a form of svadhyaya, since the effort is toward self-awareness. At its core is the value of self-education and how important it is to keep learning throughout life. Traditionally, svadhyaya encouraged studying traditional texts, including Patañjali's *Sutras* and the *Bhagavad Gita*. We recommend that you read some of the great translations (Miller, 1995, Desikachar, 1995; Deutsch, 1968). Ultimately, the lesson is to get to know yourself, and meditation is an important tool to use. Continued meditation will permit you to evolve to your full potential, while helping others to do so as well.

1. *Take a few minutes each day to sit quietly with yourself and pay attention to what you are experiencing. Write down what you notice as it is happening, following your stream of consciousness.*

2. *Read the classics: Patañjali's Sutras, the Bhagavad Gita, and the Upanishads.*

3. *Take time out of your week to pursue your intellectual interests, whatever they are. Follow up on searches online, take out books from the library, or consult experts in the field.*

Ishvara Pranidana, Attention to the Divine Within

The fifth and final niyama, ishvara pranidana, is a culmination of all that came before, with dedication to a higher power, whatever that is for you. Ishvara Pranidana reminds you to orient your life toward a higher principle. Ishvara means the unifying principle within the nature of the universe, and so being dedicated to a principle found in all that is, elevates everything you do and endows it with higher values. By attending to the divine within, you can live wholeheartedly, deeply one with your life as it is, and have faith in it. Believe in believing itself, and you open the way to believing in yourself.

1. *Open yourself to the spiritual world around you. What inspires you? Is it an awesome mountain peak or the smile of an infant? Or do you feel inspired by a great invention or powerful movie? Or perhaps you find yourself in awe of an elite athlete or great artist? Consider what speaks to you and opens your heart to the greater potentials all around you. Note these ideas in your journal.*

Ishvara Pranidana Meditation

Ishvara pranidana meditation involves contemplating the divine. If you are involved in a religious tradition, you might engage in prayer. But you can also connect with your spiritual being through nature. We have used this meditation with people of all ages, to inspire a sense of the divine in all things.

Sit quietly for several minutes on the ground outdoors. Place your hands palms down onto the ground. Let yourself sense the great mass of the earth that stretches out beneath your palms. Feel the solidity of the ground. Take a few moments to sense the mass. As you feel the support of the earth beneath you, let yourself comprehend the immensity of our earth, and how the forces of gravity are keeping you stable as you sit: Even though our planet spins and speeds through space, you are balanced and still. Marvel at this miracle as you meditate now, and experience your connection to something greater, the divine.

JOURNALING

Note ways that you are bringing the yamas and niyamas into your daily routines. For example, do you find yourself responding with more patience and moderation to a loved one's anger? Or maybe you have a time when you chose to study rather than party. Record times when you have made higher choices and performed new actions.

CHAPTER 5

Breathing (Pranayama) as the Gateway to Self-Regulation

Respiration being disturbed, the mind becomes disturbed.
By restraining respiration, the Yogi gets steadiness of mind.
—Swami Swatmarama,1914

IN THIS CHAPTER

- Study prana, the sum of all the energy and vitality in the universe and the cause of the motion of breath
- Perform several classic breathing meditations, including counting the breaths, rhythmic breathing, mind-body breathing, the complete breath, and chakra breathing
- Learn how to relax, find balance, and strengthen through breathing meditations

INTRODUCTION

Control of the breath is one of the hallmarks of yoga, and awareness of breathing is a doorway into mindfulness. Each breath you take links your inner experiencing with the outer world. Breathing is also the gateway to emotions and influences thinking, and so learning to work with the breath can have a strong influence on your psychological adjustment.

One of the goals in yoga is to control breathing as a means to regulating your body. Pranayama exercises provide a way to turn your attention to breathing so that you can voluntarily alter what is usually an involuntary process.

Breathing can be divided into four parts: (1) inhalation, when the air is brought into the body; (2) held-in-breath, the moment between breathing in and out; (3) exhalation to let air out; and (4) the pause that leads gently to a held-out breath, before the pattern repeats again.

The practice of pranayama starts with gradual changes in timing, volume, and force of your normal breathing pattern, and builds from there. By making adjustments to the parts, you gain voluntary control of the whole breathing cycle. As you become more aware of your breathing, your overall awareness deepens. And your ability to regulate yourself, even in times of stress, will improve.

The Woman Who Breathed Away Her Anxiety

"I feel a terrible constriction in my chest, and then I panic. I feel like I'm having a heart attack! I can't control it, it happens all the time, and it's ruining my life." This was the lament of our client, Linda, who sat slumped in the chair as she told us about her feelings of frustration and hopelessness. She had read about the benefits of meditation in a magazine, and decided to try it. We began with meditative breathing, and she learned to become calm during the sessions. Unfortunately, she still felt anxiety during the week. The interpretation she was giving it—a possible heart attack or serious problem—was an extremely alarming evaluation that she kept making. Her interpretation of the sensation was negative and threatening. Through this dynamic, she unwittingly intensified the uncomfortable sensations she felt.

She practiced mindful awareness in the sessions with our guidance, simply observing each sensation just as it was. She learned to be more neutral as she observed carefully, objectively, without adding negative evaluations to her situation. In time, her anxiety abated and she began to feel hopeful and optimistic for the first time in many years.

Information: The Value of Respiration

The main job of respiration is to absorb oxygen from the atmosphere into the body and to expel carbon dioxide, the waste product, from the body into the atmosphere. Oxygen is carried to every cell in the body and is a vital ingredient in keeping the body running (metabolism). Digested nutrients from food are mixed with oxygen, enzymes, and other chemicals to fuel our body. fMRI reveals a correlation between oxygen in particular areas of the brain and activation of associated functions. Breathing performs several other functions as well: carrying odor molecules from the atmosphere to be detected by the brain and using airflow through the larynx (voice box) to speak. So, you can see how respiration is vital to everything you do. Breathing is essential for life itself!

GUIDELINES FOR PRACTICE

1. Take time in performing the breathing exercises. As with any physical exercise, warming up is important. Be patient and allow yourself time to settle into the exercise.

2. You can perform many of these breathing exercises at various times and places throughout your day. In fact, you can stop for a moment at your desk, at home between things, or even in bed, morning or night. The most important thing is that you do it, whether you prefer to practice for short periods or do a longer session.

3. The body responds best to a gentle, gradual extension of its capacities, and thus breath control works well when you perform these breathing exercises gently and gradually.

4. Typically, you will breathe through your nose.

5. Beginners sometimes experience a slight dizziness. If you feel dizzy or uncomfortable with an exercise, stop for a few minutes until the dizziness or discomfort goes away and try again. Avoid pushing too hard or too fast. If dizziness persists, check with your medical doctor. Be especially careful if you have any blood pressure issues, and confirm with your doctor that it is safe for you to do yoga breathing exercises.

6. Your body knows how to breathe comfortably and how to find your natural way to breathe in a rhythm. Ultimately, the breathing pattern happens by itself, if you allow it. So, don't force anything, simply follow the instructions, and let nature take its course.

BEGINNING MEDITATIVE BREATHING

If you are new to meditation, try doing this exercise for a brief time. Set a timer for one minute and then begin. As you become comfortable with a short time, you will be able to increase the duration for longer periods. Don't force it, but be persistent.

Focus on Breathing: Counting the Breaths

Sit cross-legged on a pillow on the floor or on a chair if you find sitting on the floor uncomfortable. Keep your back relatively straight with your head facing straight ahead so that your breathing passages are open. Close your eyes and breathe gently. Allow your breathing to become soft and comfortable. Breathe in this way for several minutes, gradually finding a relaxed, easy rhythm. Then, begin silently counting each breath. Consider the entire process of inhaling, holding, and then exhaling, as one breath. Count up to ten and then begin again. If your attention wanders away from the count, gently bring it back as soon as you notice. Over time, you will stay focused on your breathing, without conscious effort.

Rhythmic Breathing 1

Now that you have kept your attention directed to your breathing, you can begin gently gaining control of your breathing patterns. These rhythmic exercises involve breathing in measured ways. By regulating your breathing, you are beginning to learn to influence the mind by means of the breath. Breath is prana, the Sanskrit word for *energy* that is comparable to the Chinese concept of chi. Regulating your breathing also stabilizes the flow of energy, bringing about balance in your nervous system.

First, inhale for four counts and then exhale for four counts. Continue to inhale for four counts and exhale for four counts. Make your breathing gentle, steady, and comfortable. Do this for several minutes. Practice at various times over several days. You can do it in many different settings, such as sitting at your desk, lying in your bed, or walking from room to room in your house. Eventually, your nervous system calms down, you enter a steady state, and you feel more rested than you usually do.

Rhythmic Breathing 2

Now, inhale slowly and gently for four counts, hold for two counts, and then slowly and gently exhale for four counts. Repeat this pattern of breathing in, holding, and then breathing out again. In this exercise, the only holding is after you inhale. Practice this at various times and in different body positions over several days.

DEVELOPING AWARENESS OF THE BREATH

Breathing is usually an unconscious process that takes care of itself. But in letting the breathing process be involuntary and unconscious, you may have formed poor breathing habits as a reflection of your inner distress. By learning to be aware of your breathing, you initiate a process of mindfulness that can be carried into every aspect of your life. Through mindful awareness, you can gently redirect your breathing in new and better habitual ways to bring about greater vitality and calm. The following two exercises turn attention to observing and experiencing breathing.

Awareness of the Breath 1: Listening to Breathing

Some people find listening to breathing comes easier than counting the breaths. Sit comfortably and close your eyes. Pay close attention to the sound of the air as it enters your nose. Keep your attention focused on the quiet in between inhaling and exhaling, and then listen carefully as the air exits again. Keep focusing attention on the sound of your breathing. If you get distracted, gently bring your attention back to the sound of your breathing.

You can hear your breathing more easily by placing your hands lightly over both of your ears. Notice how the sound becomes more pronounced. After you have done this for a short time, you will become sensitized to your breathing sounds, making it easier to stay attuned.

Awareness of the Breath 2: Following the Breath

Sit comfortably and direct your attention to your breathing. Try to relax your body and just breathe naturally and comfortably. As you inhale, notice how your rib cage expands slightly as you bring air in and down through your breathing passages. Pay attention as the air pushes out again. Keep your awareness on each new breath, in and then out as you allow the process to happen naturally. If you have any distracting thoughts, gently bring your attention back to your breathing. Let yourself experience each breath anew, as a new moment. Continue staying with your moment-by-moment breathing.

THE COMPLETE BREATH

Now that you have learned to regulate your breathing rhythms and focus your attention on breathing, you will enjoy taking a few complete breaths. Without realizing it, you may have gotten into the poor habit of holding your chest, rib cage, diaphragm, and abdomen rigid while breathing. Such inflexibility prevents a full breath from happening. As a result, energy becomes blocked or stuck, resulting in discomfort and even illness. The complete breath initiates a process to free breathing as it frees the body. The complete breath uses all the respiratory muscles optimally. By involving your breathing processes in this way, you can release unnecessary tension, allowing energy to flow naturally and freely.

A complete breath naturally brings about movement of the chest, rib cage, diaphragm, and abdomen. When done correctly, the complete breath fills the lungs, expanding them forward, sideways, and backward. The complete breath can be performed standing up, lying down, or sitting. We offer instructions for standing and sitting, but please feel free to try it when lying down as well.

Standing Complete Breath

Stand comfortably upright. Slowly begin inhaling. Bring the air in through your nose and send it down into your lungs, raising your rib cage as you lift your arms out to your sides, extending them with hands open, palms toward the front. Allow your abdomen to swell while your rib cage expands. Fill your lungs completely, then slowly exhale, dropping your rib cage from the bottom. Push the air up from below and out through your nose until all the air is completely expelled from your lungs.

Inhalation and exhalation should be evenly timed, with a slight pause between each. You may want to count to four as you inhale and then four as you exhale. You can breathe for up to six counts. Do what feels comfortable. Those capable of more advanced breathing exercises may add a pause between inhalation and exhalation, but the pause is minimal.

Work to keep the time that you spend inhaling and exhaling equal. This may mean shortening exhalation or lengthening inhalation. Try this out for yourself. Listen to your own inner rhythms. Even though you are deliberately breathing in a pattern, keep it as relaxed and natural as possible. You should not feel as if you are forcing your breath. Don't breathe in a strained, hard, or sudden manner. As your breathing becomes more balanced and comfortable, you will begin to feel more relaxed and calm.

Coordinating Body Movement with the Standing Complete Breath

Coordinating breathing with body positioning extends breathing into your body. You may also find it easier to stay focused by adding a body motion to each breath.

For a complete breath while standing, use your arms to help. Stand with your feet together, hands at your sides, and palms facing in toward your body. Let your head sag forward slightly and exhale. Slowly begin inhaling as you raise your arms out from your sides, arms straight with palms up. Let your lungs completely fill with air when your hands meet up above your head. Hold for a moment and then slowly begin exhaling as you lower your arms. All of the air should be expelled when your arms are back down at your sides.

Sitting Complete Breath

The complete breath can also be done sitting. Find a comfortable seated posture. Begin by inhaling. When you are first learning, in order to feel the motion as you breathe, place the palms of your relaxed hands on your upper abdomen. Your hands should move with your abdomen as it expands and your lungs fill with air. As you exhale and bring your rib cage toward your spine, keep your hands in place.

Not only is expanding the abdomen part of the complete breath, the diaphragm, rib cage, and chest are also involved. Place your hands on your diaphragm/rib cage area to feel this part of the breath. As you inhale again, feel how your diaphragm naturally expands downward as your ribs raise. Your chest also expands and your shoulders rise slightly. The complete inhalation, done correctly, will bring about movement in your abdomen, diaphragm, ribs, chest, and shoulders. Note the moment between inhaling and exhaling, and then exhale by allowing your chest and rib cage to drop and your shoulders to sink. Finally, lightly tighten your upper abdominal muscles to help push the last bit of air out with exhalation. One sequence of a complete breath entails inhaling, holding, and exhaling.

WORKING WITH PRANA

According to yogic theory, prana has three primary channels that the life-energy flows through: ida, with access through the left nostril for the lunar energy flowing along the left side of the body; pingala, with access through the right nostril for the solar energy, flowing along the right side of the body; and sushumna. When you breathe through both nostrils together evenly, you harmonize the life force through *sushumna*, the channel that flows down the center of your body, then runs along your spinal cord. Sushumna is the route by which coiled kundalini energy rises and awakens the universal light of higher consciousness. All of these channels are part of what is known as *the subtle body*.

Alternate Nostril Breathing

Breathing through both nostrils evenly, you balance your energy. This nostril breathing exercise brings you into balance by opening both nostrils to take in and expel air evenly.

Begin by curling your fingers of your right hand as you hold your right thumb out. Place your right thumb over your right nostril and inhale, exhale, and inhale again out of the open left nostril.

FIGURE 5.1 Nostril Breathing 1

Then slide the crook of your bent index finger to close your left nostril and exhale, inhale, and exhale.

Without pause, slide your thumb over your right nostril again and repeat the pattern. Move from one nostril to the other in this way. Repeat the pattern for several minutes. Then breathe out of both nostrils together. You will experience openness and balance in your breathing, and a sense of energy and emotional balance overall.

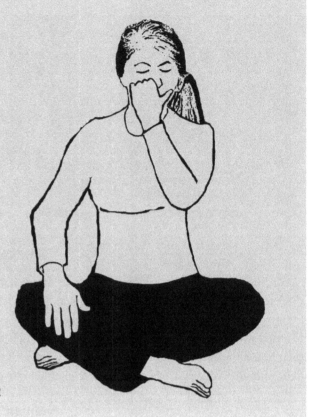

FIGURE 5.2 Nostril Breathing 2

Activate the Kundalini

The three energy channels come together at seven different centers in the body, known as chakras, represented as lotuses. Each chakra has a location in the body and is associated with a color, a number of lotus pedals, and certain physical and psychological properties. Meditations are directed to a particular center of energy and move up through the chain, to raise energy and connect with the universal principle of higher consciousness. Kundalini yoga refers to this process as raising the kundalini energy, sometimes symbolized as a serpent, up from the bottom of the spine and out through the head.

Kundalini energy is believed to be the natural energy stored at the base of the spine in the root chakra, muladhara, in a coil. Activating kundalini will give a feeling of energy to the whole body. Once you become comfortable with this exercise, you will be able to direct the energy to different chakra energy centers to enhance therapeutic work. We offer specific chakra energy meditations to help with problems covered in Part III.

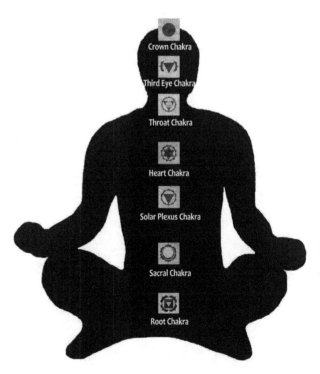

FIGURE 5.3 All the Chakras

Begin sitting in an easy pose, with your spine fairly upright and direct your eyes to look straight ahead. Breathe comfortably, balancing your breathing evenly between both nostrils. Perform this breathing for several minutes until you can allow the air to flow through both nostrils evenly. As you continue breathing comfortably, visualize energy flowing up the left side of your spine, rising up from the root chakra. Follow the energy as it flows all the way up through each chakra to the crown chakra at the top of your head, sahasrara chakra. Then, visualize the energy flowing from left to right at the center of the chakra and down the right side of your spine, back to the root chakra. Now imagine the energy flowing around, under the root chakra, to the left side, and then back up again through your body. Repeat the cycle naturally and comfortably for several minutes.

Information Box: The Chakras

Muladhara chakra with 4 lotus petals is the root chakra, located at the base of the spine and associated with the color red, which symbolizes stability, sensuality, and spiritual security. Svadhisthana chakra has 6 lotus petals and is found in the lower abdomen between the belly button and the pelvic bone. Often linked to sexuality, this chakra is orange and associated with relationships, emotions, and creativity. Manipura chakra has 10 lotus petals and is positioned at the bottom of the rib cage. It is yellow in color, plays a role in digestion, and symbolizes self-esteem, energy, and personal empowerment. Anahata chakra, the heart chakra with 12 lotus petals, found at the heart in the center of the chest, is green and symbolizes love, compassion, equilibrium, acceptance, and trust. Vishuddha chakra is the throat chakra with 16 lotus petals. It is located in the throat, with a light turquoise blue color, and symbolizes communication, expression, faith, and inspiration. Ajna chakra is situated above the bridge of the nose between the eyebrows, with 2 lotus petals, an indigo blue color. It is symbolic of intelligence, intuition, and trusting inner wisdom. The highest chakra, sahasrara chakra has 1,000 lotus petals, is located at the top of the head with a white or violet color, and is thought to be the chakra of pure consciousness. Here we find spiritual understanding and its expression in selfless devotion and inspiration.

FIGURE 5.4 Root Chakra

FIGURE 5.5 Sacral Chakra

FIGURE 5.6 The Solar Plexus Chakra

FIGURE 5.7 The Heart Chakra

FIGURE 5.8 The Throat Chakra

FIGURE 5.9 The Third Eye Chakra

FIGURE 5.10 The Crown Chakra

Raising the Kundalini

Perform this exercise following activating kundalini, breathing through both nostrils together. Pay close attention to your body. Imagine and feel energy flowing through you while you breathe with relaxed, normal breaths. Visualize your energy invigorating your entire body.

Once you can visualize the energy flowing around, beginning from the root chakra, picture the energy flowing up and into each chakra (see Figure 5.3). Focus attention on each area, one at a time, as you breathe comfortably. Imagine the energy flowing around in the area as you breathe, and then picture it moving up to the next chakra. If you notice any areas where the flow of your energy seems blocked, perhaps you are unnecessarily tensing. Let go of the tension in that area and then allow the energy that gets released to flow freely up to the next chakra. Follow the chain up through your body until you see the energy entering the highest chakra at the top of your head. Feel the energy flowing at the crown of your head. This phase of the meditation will bring a feeling of great happiness and peace. Enjoy the experience!

JOURNALING

1. General observations
   a. Record what you experienced with each exercise.
   b. Do you find some of the exercises easier than others?

2. Counting the breaths
   a. Were you able to keep your attention on counting or did it wander?
   b. How did you notice that your attention had wandered?
   c. How did you bring it back to counting?
      i. Were you able to be gentle and kind to yourself or were you harsh and judgmental? If you observe that you were hard on yourself, work on being more forgiving and tolerant. Remind yourself that you are engaged in a learning process.

3. Rhythmic breathing exercises
   a. How did it feel as you synchronized your breathing to a count?
   b. Were you able to keep your breathing natural and comfortable as you counted or did it feel forced? If you felt some tension, keep working on making your breathing comfortable and relaxed even though you are adding a constraint through counting.

4. Awareness of the breath
   a. What did you observe as you turned your attention to the different aspects of breathing, its sound and sense?

5. The complete breath
   a. Note any places where you might be tightening your breathing passages, restricting the natural flow of breath. Can you allow these areas to release?
   b. Notice your energy before and after performing a few complete breaths. Do you experience any increase in vitality?

6. Energy exercises: Alternate nostril breathing and kundalini

CHARTING

Fill out the chart for each of the five types of breathing exercises you practiced in this chapter. We encourage you to continue doing these exercises regularly. They are always a resource! You will incorporate these and other variations in the application chapters.

FIGURE 5.11 Chart Your Breathing Experience

	Ease of exercise (1 = easy, 5 = difficult)	Number of times attention wandered	Ease of breathing (1 = natural, 5 = forced)	Amount of time practicing this meditation	Energy level following exercise (1 = low, 5 = high)
Counting the Breaths					
Rhythmic Breathing					
Awareness of the Breath					
Complete Breath					
Nostril Breathing					
Kundalini Breathing					

CHAPTER 6

Postures (Asanas) for Therapeutic Work Through the Body

In our practice we concentrate on the body, the breath, and the mind.
Our senses are included as part of the mind. Although it theoretically
appears possible for body, breath, and mind to work independent of
one another, the purpose of yoga is to unify their actions.

—Desikachar, 1995

IN THIS CHAPTER

- Discover why adding bodywork to therapy is so helpful
- Transform everyday postures—standing, sitting and lying prone—into yoga asanas
- Perform simple yoga asanas to engage the body right in the therapy office as part of the session or at home between sessions
- Train in specific yoga postures, unifying mind, brain, and body to bring about emotional change

INTRODUCTION

Everything we do in life involves taking one of three fundamental postures: standing, sitting, or lying prone. As we hold and move through those postures, we take part in our world.

Yoga asanas are always based on one of these fundamental postures, with many creative combinations and variations; however, one important quality of yoga asanas makes them different from the postures you use in everyday life: unified awareness. Typically, you probably pay little attention to how your body is positioned unless it becomes a problem for you. But when practicing yoga postures, you deliberately place your body into a position, hold it, bring your attention to it, and synchronize your breathing with it.

Holding your body in position in this way has many specific and nonspecific therapeutic benefits. Even though therapy typically transpires in the sitting posture and/or sometimes from a lying prone position, you can extend the therapeutic effect of bodywork by working with different yoga postures.

Mr. Spock Learns the Value of Feeling

A graduate student was working on his PhD in mathematics. He told us that he liked his adviser, the university, and his area of study. And yet, he felt anxious, and his anxiety was becoming worse. When he sat down to study, his anxiety levels increased. He told us that his friends called him Mr. Spock because he tended to be logical. He wasn't too sure about psychotherapy but felt desperate enough to try anything. True to his nickname, he said, "I'm coming to see you because meditation seems like the logical thing to do." He was factual in the account of his life and his concerns, with no reference to feelings except for anxiety. He told us he didn't have time to exercise, nor had he ever liked it much. In fact, he hardly moved as he spoke.

We began his meditation training by teaching him to attend to simple, everyday postures: standing, sitting, and lying prone. He found that having something definite to focus on was helpful. We encouraged him to notice his body sensations in each position, such as body temperature, heartbeat, and body alignment from head to toe. He focused on his breathing and learned to relax his breath. In time, he began to notice that he was holding his body rigidly and felt interested in learning some yoga stretches. We taught him the triangle pose and sun salutation, which he could practice intermittently during the long hours he spent at his lab. Gradually he felt more comfortable physically and his anxiety lessened. We also talked about finding a better balance for his life, which included his body and his emotions in attunement with his mind. Interestingly, he told us at his closing session that he now felt some of the mathematical insights that he was working into his dissertation as body sensations. He believed his intellectual work was enriched by his meditative practice.

BENEFITS OF YOGA POSTURES FOR THERAPY

The following list includes a number of important benefits to integrating yoga postures into therapy.

1. **Unify mind, body, and breath.** Often when people are suffering from stress, trauma, anxiety, depression, and addiction, they have been out of touch with their physical responses, dissociated from the broad range of possible experiences, and instead remain narrowly focused on the discomforts. Linking mind with body through mindful awareness of body postures and gentle breathing can lessen your feelings of distress by rebalancing nervous system reactions. At the same time, your attention becomes free to perceive more clearly and fully.

2. **Work on problems indirectly through the body.** Your psychological disturbances are also expressed in your body, and so working on the body level provides a new doorway to change. Body sensing can loosen old patterns and form healthier ones. New feelings emerge naturally and automatically. When you take on a new posture, you might find yourself feeling more self-confident, competent, and calm. Such feelings occur bottom-up as a direct response, setting in motion a process of inner development and integration.

3. **Bring about balance and stay centered.** Therapy helps people find balance. Talking therapies bring this about through better thinking and improved emotional regulation, but you can influence balance directly through bodywork. People often neglect their posture, a key element of balance, and find themselves burdened with aches, pains, and fatigue. Postural aberrations force you to fight against gravity, thereby dissipating your energy. When you are able to center your body as you go through your day, gravity becomes your ally, and body positioning during action becomes effortless. Yoga poses are designed to bring about general body balance, and in the process, foster emotional balance as well. Through balancing your body, you can find your center. This centered feeling can become a resource for self-regulation, a comforting zero-point to return to when you are feeling disturbed.

As you perform a yoga posture, first on one side and then on the other, you may notice that each side of your body is different. Most people find that positions are easier on one side than the other. In fact, people often favor one side over the other. Yoga works on both sides equally, helping to strengthen the weaker side. By using both sides of your body, the two hemispheres of your brain are stimulated. Eventually, mind, brain, and body become integrated, working together for optimal functioning.

4. **Produce a dual effect of alertness with relaxation.** The practice of yoga postures has a dual effect, shared by many meditation methods, of alertness combined with relaxation. Often when we are trying to accomplish something, we are alert but we are also tense. Meditation teaches how to be alert while being relaxed. Relaxed alertness can help to reduce stress because it increases a person's ability to handle challenges. Patañjali's *Yoga Sutra* described these two qualities as the key to performing yoga postures: sthira (alertness) and sukha (relaxation). "These qualities can be achieved by recognizing and observing the reactions of the body and the breath to the various postures that comprise *asana* practice. Once known, these reactions can be controlled step-by-step. . . *Asanas* must have the dual qualities of alertness and relaxation. . .When these principles are correctly followed, *asana* practice will help a person endure and even minimize the external influences on the body such as age, climate, diet, and work" (*Yoga Sutras of Patañjali* in Desikachar, 1995, 180–181). Thus, learning to be both alert and relaxed while performing a posture can have a positive effect that generalizes to everyday life.

5. **Even simple postures can be therapeutic.** Hatha yoga classes will move you through a variety of postures. When you apply the principles of yoga and unify mind and body with breathing, even simple body positions—such as standing, sitting, or lying prone with some easy bends and twists—can elicit therapeutic effects. If you already practice Hatha yoga, you can use all the postures you know. But if you are not a yoga practitioner, use your natural body positioning, with some minor adjustments, to foster mindful mind-body unity.

TIP: **Asanas involve more than moving the body into a posture and holding it there.** Each asana contains three aspects: (1) moving into the pose, (2) holding the pose, and (3) coming out of the pose. Each aspect is important. So, when you perform the movements, be mindful that coming into and out of the pose is part of the process. Move gracefully, calmly, without rushing, and with balance and poise. Even when you are performing postures quickly, maintain gracefulness and control without straining.

TIP: **Start from where you are.** Begin with what you can do comfortably, without straining. Even if you are barely in the posture, but you have no discomfort, you are embarking on the path. If you are feeling tension, ease back until the posture can be held without strain. Work gradually, accept yourself, and your capacities will expand.

STANDING POSTURES

Standing postures can be an important part of a therapeutic yoga practice. Much of our life is spent standing. We balance upright and walk from the standing position. We gauge where we are and orient perceptually from our height. Often, we take for granted standing up, giving it little thought. But symbolically, to stand on your own two feet indicates independence and competence. Coming to an alert, aligned standing posture is a key to finding balance in your life.

How can you become more aligned? Simply standing or sitting upright by means of discipline is not the answer. Bring awareness to your body to find the answers. In the process, you develop new sensitivities.

Discover Your Balance in Mountain Pose (Standing)

This series of exercises will help you discover your best standing posture, known in yoga as the mountain pose, tadasana. First, you will work with overall balance, and then you will refine your standing pose to be comfortably upright and relaxed.

Discover your optimal alignment with gravity, just standing upright with awareness. Begin the process by standing with your feet together, ankles touching, and arms at your sides. If you feel uncomfortable, you can move your feet slightly apart. Stand up straight, but not stiffly. Keep your shoulders from slumping, and don't let your back hunch. Look straight ahead, keeping your head upright and centered. Breathe comfortably and focus your attention on standing.

Now, move your legs slightly apart, approximately shoulder width apart. Place your weight evenly between both feet. Rock gently from side to side and feel your balance point shifting first to one leg and then to the other. Stop for a moment with your weight more on one foot and pay attention to how that side feels.

How long does it feel, from your ankle to the floor, from your knee to the floor, from your hip to the floor, and from your shoulder to the floor? Without moving, turn your attention to your other leg that has less weight on it. Do you perceive the two legs differently? Now rock gently back and forth several times. You will discover a place exactly between your two legs where balance is effortless and shared by both legs equally. Stand for a moment or two as you sense this balance point.

Next, try rocking very slightly forward and back.

You will feel some muscles tighten up as you shift forward and backward. As before, compare the length of the front of your body with the length of the back of your body. Now rock just a little, very gently, forward and back. Notice the point at which your muscles relax and your feet are firmly planted on the ground.

Just stand for a moment in that place between side-to-side and forward-and-back, where you are most relaxed, balanced, and aligned with gravity.

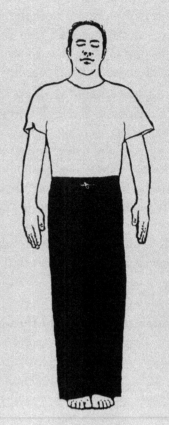

FIGURE 6.1 Just Standing

FIGURE 6.2 Shifting Weight

FIGURE 6.3 Rocking Forward and Back

Refine your Mountain Pose 1 (Knees)

To refine your standing posture even further, find the best position for your knees, somewhere between bent and flexed. Begin by slightly bending your knees, keeping them directly over your ankles. Then, straighten them, flexing gently. Go back and forth between bending and straightening, discovering the point between, where your knees feel comfortably aligned and relaxed.

FIGURE 6.4 Bending Knees   **FIGURE 6.5** Flexing Knees

Refine Your Mountain Pose 2

Now push your pelvic area back slightly, letting your back arch a bit, feeling which muscles tighten as you do so. Then lightly push your pelvis forward, rounding your back slightly. Keep your attention on how your muscles feel as you gently move your pelvis forward and back several times, until you find that place in between, where everything feels relaxed. Stand for a moment and notice your body position.

FIGURE 6.6 Arched Back   **FIGURE 6.7** Rounded Back

Refine Your Mountain Pose 3

Rotate your shoulders forward and back feeling your upper back round and arch gently as you move. You will discover a comfortable place where your shoulders are aligned and comfortable. Notice your standing now.

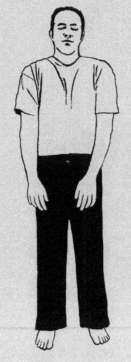

FIGURE 6.8 Shoulders Forward

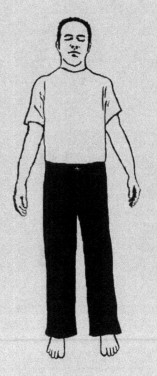

FIGURE 6.9 Shoulders Back

Refine Your Mountain Pose 4

Finally, tilt your head from side to side until you discover the point at which your neck feels most comfortable. Then tilt your head forward and back slightly until you find the relaxed upright position for your head and neck.

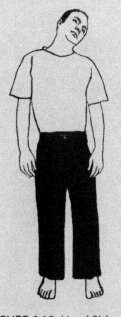

FIGURE 6.10 Head Sideways

SITTING POSITIONS

A common stereotype of the asana used for yoga and mindfulness is to be seated cross-legged on the floor in an upright position. This practice derives from a tradition in India where people sat on the floor as part of their daily routines. But today, we are more accustomed to sitting in chairs, and some might feel awkward having to sit on the floor to do yoga and mindfulness. Fortunately, you can still practice, even if you are not able to sit comfortably cross-legged on the floor. Many of the sitting postures can be adapted to sitting in a chair, so long as you position your body correctly. Some of these adaptations are given later in this chapter. You may think of others.

Beginners who sit on the floor will find it easier to use a firm cushion that will raise their hips three to six inches. There are special cushions made for meditation. Using one can take the strain off the lower back and knees, making sitting on the floor easier. Eventually you may discover that you can sit comfortably without a pillow.

You should feel at ease with your posture for sitting. If you are bothered by how you feel when you attempt to sit in meditation, you may lose your concentration. Since concentration is important for making progress, take some time to find the most comfortable sitting position. As you become more flexible, varied positions will become easier to do.

Coming Mindfully to Sitting from Standing

Place a chair behind you and stand in mountain pose, focusing on your posture as you breathe naturally for several minutes. Then, after you have attuned to standing, stay attuned as you sit down into the chair. Notice how you move from the standing pose to the sitting pose. We encourage you to try this exercise in different ways: from standing to sitting on the floor, if you are able, or from standing to sitting on a chair. Let your breathing naturally coordinate with your movement. Keep your head gracefully poised upright, neck lightly stretched upward and not tensed, with chin lifted slightly. Then, when you are seated, move on to the next exercise to find your optimal sitting position.

Traditional Cross-Legged Positions

Energy flows around and within the body, leaving through the hands and the feet. When seated cross-legged, energy can flow in a circle, continually nourishing the body rather than escaping. Thus, many traditional sitting positions are performed with legs crossed in various ways.

Easy Pose, Sukhasana

One of the easiest sitting positions is called easy pose. The easy pose is very similar to the cross-legged position you may have used as a child when sitting on the floor.

Draw your left foot in until the heel is as far under your right thigh as possible without forcing it. Then draw the right foot under the left thigh in the same way. Let your hands rest on your knees. Your legs will be crossed at the ankles. Most important is that you keep your spine, neck, and head balanced and held upright. This pose should be easy to maintain over an extended period.

FIGURE 6.11 Cross-Legged Floor Sitting Posture

Chair Sitting Position

When performing a yoga pose sitting in a chair, keep your spine, neck, and head upright just as in the floor-sitting positions. Make sure your thighs are parallel to the floor and lower legs perpendicular to the floor.

If the chair is too high to do this, you may need to place a book or pillow under your feet on the floor to raise them up. Let your hands rest on your knees, with your arms away from your rib cage.

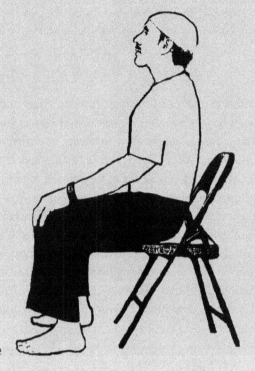

FIGURE 6.12 Chair Sitting Posture

Finding Your Balanced Sitting Position

This exercise guides you in discovering alignment with gravity for the most comfortable sitting position. Sit cross-legged on the floor or on a small cushion. If floor sitting is uncomfortable, sit in a straight-backed chair, or perhaps on a low stool. Allow your arms to rest on your knees, and close your eyes. Rock back and forth gently and feel your sitting bones.

Experiment with swaying forward-and-back and then side-to-side as in the standing exercise to find your center. From this centered position, sit upright without being rigid, to allow your breathing passages to be open, permitting the air to flow freely in and out. Align your head upright in relation to your body, keeping your neck and shoulders as relaxed as possible. Maintain the position with your back comfortably straight and shoulders open without hunching forward.

FIGURE 6.13 Seated Rocking Sideways

Lotus Pose, Padmasana

For those who take yoga classes, you might want to sit in the classic lotus pose. Lotus pose is an ancient position described in the *Hatha Yoga Pradipika*. Some people find the lotus position easy to do without effort. Other people find it difficult because of their body type or level of flexibility. Keep in mind that comfort is always important, so don't try to force your body into this position if it does not feel good.

To perform the lotus pose, place your right foot on the left thigh and the left foot on the right thigh. Your legs are locked, making it easy to maintain over time (as long as the position is comfortable). Let your hands rest palms up on your knees. Touch your thumb to your index finger, forming a circle.

FIGURE 6.14 Lotus Pose

Kneeling Pelvic Pose, Vajrasana

Some people like to kneel, and yoga has such a sitting pose, the pelvic pose, vajrasana.

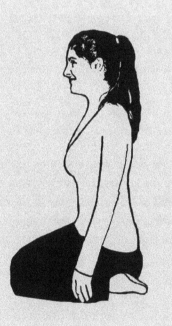

Kneel on the floor and then sit upright back on your heels. To be more comfortable, place a small cushion under the backs of your legs. Some people prefer this position to the cross-legged postures. Let your body be your guide as to how to sit most comfortably.

FIGURE 6.15 Kneeling Pelvic Pose

Lying Prone

To know ourselves means to know our relationship with the world—
not only with the world of ideas and people, but also with nature, with
the things we possess. That is our life—life being relationship to the whole.
                                                                —J. Krishnamurti 1968, 94

Life is always about relationship. When lying down, there is a relationship to the supporting surface. You can learn about yourself through this relationship. The exercises for lying down are usually performed on a thin mat on the floor, but you can also use a couch in your office or home. Try to avoid an overly soft surface. Yoga mats are designed with the correct hardness.

Several of the classic postures performed lying down can be used to relax. Savasana and crocodile pose can relax the body from head to foot. These poses can be used for deep relaxation at appropriate times during the day, or to return to your calm center after deep emotional work.

Prone Pose, Savasana

The savasana pose can help you rejuvenate and revitalize. Being very restful, savasana can help to bring about a feeling of well-being.

Lie down on your back on the floor with your legs extended and arms at your side, palms facing up. Let your feet move apart and rotate slightly outward. Close your eyes.

FIGURE 6.16 Savasana Lying Prone

Breathe comfortably. Scan your body with your attention and let go of any unnecessary tensions. If you experience tightening in the muscles of your face, stomach, neck, shoulders, or back, inhale, hold the muscles slightly, and exhale gently, letting the tension go a little with each exhalation. Try to permit as much relaxation as you can. Rest in this position for a few minutes.

If you feel tightness in your lower back in this asana, you can modify it by raising your knees while resting your feet flat on the floor. You may want to put a pillow under your knees and let your legs extend comfortably. This tends to flatten the lower back, allowing it to relax very deeply. As you feel your back muscles relax, you may be able to extend your legs flat into the corpse pose. If not, use the modified position when needed to allow yourself to relax.

Crocodile Pose, Makarasana

The crocodile pose is also a relaxation posture, performed lying on your stomach. According to Indian folklore, the crocodile is considered one of nature's most extraordinary creatures because it can be comfortable on the earth as well as in the water. Thus this pose symbolizes being able to fully relax under any circumstance. The crocodile pose can be helpful to the digestive system, massaging the abdomen slightly. Some people may find this pose more comfortable than savasana. If this is so for you, use the crocodile pose instead for deep relaxation.

Lie facedown on the floor. Let your legs stretch apart at a comfortable distance with your heels facing in and toes pointing out. Bend one arm to make a resting place for your forehead, placing your hand on your opposite shoulder, forming a triangle. Let your other hand come across your body at shoulder level and grasp the opposite shoulder. This position keeps your arms from moving as you totally relax.

FIGURE 6.17 Crocodile Lying Prone Facedown

Once you are in position, let your body relax completely. Gently breathe in and out as you let go of any unnecessary tensions. Try to keep your inhalation and exhalation approximately the same length. Remain relaxed in this position for a few minutes.

Using Postures to Elicit a New Experience

Attitudes and feelings are expressed in how you hold your body. If you are feeling self-confident, you tend to stand upright, with shoulders squared, and rib cage lifted, whereas when feeling insecure or frightened, you might hunch forward or look down. The effect is reciprocal and so, by altering your posture, you can elicit a different emotional experience. The following poses are some examples of ways you can elicit feelings:

1. Confidence, warrior pose
2. Security and self-soothing, child pose
3. Flexibility, triangle pose

Many other poses can elicit helpful feelings. Now that you understand the principle, we encourage you to experiment to find what works best for you.

Taking a Confident Stance in the Warrior Pose

Confidence is reflected in how you hold your body. The warrior pose develops strength in your feet, arches, calves, and thighs. It also works the abdomen and shoulders. The position is symbolic of taking a strong stance, and you will feel your strength build as you embody this posture.

Begin by stepping your right leg out approximately three feet from your left leg. Bend your right, front knee, keeping the lower leg perpendicular and your thigh parallel to the floor so that your bent leg forms as close to a 90-degree angle as possible. Your left leg at the rear should be relatively straight and your left foot should be perpendicular to your right foot. Keep your hips level. As you move your feet into position, bring your arms up overhead. Then spread your arms out from your sides, directly over your legs, parallel to the floor with fingers held together and pointing straight out. Turn your head to face your front leg, keeping your neck and back straight. Lift your chest and stretch out through your arms and fingers. Focus your eyes facing forward as you hold the position and breathe in and out for as long as you can without discomfort.

Move slowly in and out of each position, keeping your motions smooth. Hold the posture for several minutes if you can, breathing gently, and then slowly switch sides moving the left leg out front.

FIGURE 6.18 Warrior Pose

Self-Soothing and Feeling Secure: The Child Pose

Child pose offers a feeling of self-support that can be reassuring especially after dealing with disturbing emotions. You may also combine the child pose with savasana or crocodile pose, described earlier, to enhance the effect.

Sit on your feet in the pelvic pose, kneeling position. Bend forward slowly until your head touches the floor. Allow your arms to rest comfortably at your sides with your elbows bent so that they can rest on the floor.

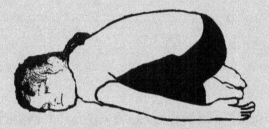

FIGURE 6.19 Child Pose

You may need to shift or move slightly to find the most comfortable position. Breathe in a soft rhythm. Rest in this position

Flexibility with the Triangle Pose

Narrow, rigid attitudes are often reflected in the body, which may become rigid and inflexible, like the attitude. You can start the process of loosening the hold of rigid perceptions by the simple act of stretching your body.

Place your legs approximately two feet apart, raise your arms out sideways to shoulder height, and inhale. Slowly bend to the left, keeping your arms stretched out and begin exhaling. Rotate your left hand down to lightly grasp your left leg as your right arm comes overhead and is pointing straight up as you continue to bend sideways.

From this position, relax your neck muscles and any other muscles that are not involved in this stretch and breathe normally. Slowly straighten as you inhale again and return to the starting position. Repeat the same motion on the other side.

Perform each movement slowly, with your mind fully focused. Don't force the stretch and only go as far as you can comfortably. Pay attention to the subtle differences in tension and relaxation of various muscles. Observe sensations and positioning. Notice how your breathing affects your body position. Stay fully attentive and do not ignore your body's counter reactions, and you will derive deep benefit. From the simple comes the profound.

FIGURE 6.20 Triangle Pose

JOURNALING

1. Observe what you experienced following each exercise.

2. Notice which postures felt most comfortable and which ones were more difficult for you.

3. Make note of what areas of your body seemed chronically tight. Were some areas flexible?

4. Were you able to coordinate your breathing with the pose?

5. When did you keep your mind focused on the posture and when did it wander? If your mind wandered, what were your associations? Be curious and open, and observe objectively. Trust that the pieces of the puzzle of your inner being will emerge if you are accepting and supportive, and it will be more likely to happen.

CHAPTER 7

Withdrawing Attention (Pratyahara) for Inner Control

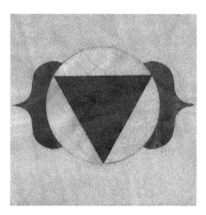

*He who has faith, who is intent on it (knowledge) and who has controlled his senses,
obtrains knowledge, and having obtained it, goes quickly to the highest peace.*

—Bhagavad Gita

In This Chapter

- Make the transition from breathing and posture practice to meditation
- Explore the two sides of withdrawal: doing and not doing
- Gain control over the distractions of external stimuli
- Discover how calm awareness develops with practice

Introduction

Yoga and mindfulness teach you how to maintain control over what the ancients called the *mind stuff* and what we today refer to as stream of thought. The process begins with what is known in yoga as pratyahara, a set of meditations that teach you how to withdraw attention and turn it inward.

In everyday life, the senses are turned outward toward the material world. According to yoga philosophy, turning the senses outward distracts us from spiritual realities and higher consciousness. Yoga trains and disciplines the mind to observe without the senses or subjective consciousness intervening so that nothing interferes with direct perception. When your mind is withdrawn and disengaged, your consciousness is freed for meditation. This is achieved by the practice of pratyahara.

Everyone can benefit from an occasional time-out. As Wordsworth once said, "The world is too much with us." Taking some time away from your busy day to practice pratyahara is renewing. Being able to deliberately withdraw your attention when needed also has therapeutic advantages. There are circumstances when you must endure a painful or difficult situation that can't be changed. Or perhaps you have disturbing thoughts that you can't put out of your mind. Or maybe you are easily distracted. This skill can be applied to help you handle difficulties so that you can meet adversity well. These inwardly focused, quiet meditative moments can add a new dimension to your life. You will develop greater self-control and a deep, lasting peace of mind.

The Girl Who Came Back to Her Life

A young girl came in to see us in a carefully matched outfit from shoes to purse to scarf. She told us that she was a planner. She liked things to be in order and lived her life in an organized way. She had just graduated from college and had a job all lined up for the fall. This summer she was doing temporary work to cover expenses. Even though everything seemed to be going well, Andrea was deluged with disturbing thoughts. She became obsessed with these thoughts until she would break down in tears. The thoughts haunted and frightened her. She tried to argue with her disturbing thoughts, because she knew they weren't true, and even if they were, it didn't matter. And yet, the more she thought about them, the more upset she became.

Andrea was a good candidate for pratyahara. She learned to withdraw her attention from outer objects, and redirect it at will. As her skills for external focus improved, she worked on withdrawing her attention from internal objects that vied for her attention, such as her thoughts. At first, this was difficult, because they seemed so real, and they had been with her for so long. We introduced her to mindfulness meditation to help her pay closer attention to her experience. As she became more focused, she had an insight: "I'm so wrapped up in my thoughts that I'm missing out on my life!" In time, as she gave less attention to her thoughts and more attention to the actual details of her life, the thoughts gradually faded and became easier to dismiss. Eventually, she was able to live in the present moment and truly enjoy it.

THE TWO SIDES

Pratyahara has two sides: not doing and doing. Withdrawing from distraction and unnecessary thought is "not doing." By withdrawing from involvement in less important concerns, energy is conserved and consciousness is freed for positive use. Actively focusing inward and pinpointing the light of consciousness toward concerns that matter is the "doing" side. You can enhance your mental abilities by practicing both sides. Then meditation and mindfulness become easier to achieve.

Tips

- Allocate a few minutes of the day for pratyahara exercise.
- Pratyahara can be done in the morning, night, or after work.
- There is a natural rhythm for you, times when you might feel like withdrawing. Use those moments to practice pratyahara.
- Lie quietly and relax. At first, your thoughts may wander. Be patient, and you will be rewarded.

Pratyahara Warm-Up

Pratyahara is the practice of withdrawing your attention from distractions, either from outer concerns and turning it inward, or from inner concerns and turning it outward, so it can be focused on more enlightened states of mind. Here is an easy way to begin the practice of withdrawal from distracting concerns.

Pour yourself a cool glass of water. Now, turn your attention to the glass as you pick it up. Feel the glass in your hand. Raise the glass to your lips. Do you feel the coolness of the glass as you take a sip? Pay attention to the water as it sits for a moment in your mouth. How does your mouth feel? Swallow the water and keep your attention focused on the cool sensation as the water travels down your throat to your stomach. Stay with the internal sensations as long as you can feel them. This exercise sets you on the path to pratyahara as you have successfully brought your attention from the outer world to your inner sensations.

PRATYAHARA PRACTICE

Now you can begin to withdraw your attention. These exercises guide you through the process. Practice each one at different times and in different settings.

Withdrawing the Senses

Begin by listening to the sounds outside. You might need to open a window. Notice what you hear, see, or smell. As you do so, let your breathing be relaxed and allow your body to become comfortable. Then withdraw your attention from these outer stimuli and bring your attention closer, to the immediate surroundings in the room. Notice as many details as you can: the temperature, the sounds that you hear, the objects that you see around you, the texture of the surface that you are sitting on, and the smells in the room. The outside stimuli will begin to fade away into the background as your immediate, closer surroundings become foreground. Continue to breathe comfortably and relax as you focus your attention on the room and what is within it.

Narrow the field even more by turning your attention away from the room and toward your inner experience of body sensations. You might find it easier to close your eyes now. Begin with your skin and notice if it feels warm or cool. Do you notice any other sensations? Breathe and relax. Concentrate on your muscles. Are some muscles tight and others loose? Moving inward, notice your heartbeat, your breathing, any sensations in your stomach. As you turn your attention inward, the sights and sounds of the room will begin to fade. Breathe comfortably and let your attention focus deeper inward.

Finally, focus on simply being calm and quiet. Sustain this tranquil, inwardly focused attention until you feel ready to stop. By withdrawing your senses stepwise from the outer environment, while simultaneously calming your energy with quiet breathing and relaxed muscles, you will develop a comfortably poised awareness. From the doing and not-doing practices of pratyahara, you are now ready to concentrate, contemplate, and meditate.

Strengthening Inner Attention Through Your Body

Begin by turning your attention away from the outer world toward the inner experience of your body. Notice what sensations you have there. Begin at your head. Pay attention to the boundaries of your face and neck. How are you holding your muscles? Are you tightening them unnecessarily? If possible, relax any unnecessary tightness that you notice.

Now direct your attention toward your shoulders. Mentally trace the width of your shoulders. Notice whether you are holding these muscles tightly. If so, let go. Continue down through your body, paying close attention to each area and then trying to relax any tension in that area. You may be surprised to notice sections that are tensed needlessly. If your attention wanders away from your body to outer concerns, bring it back. But don't force yourself to relax. Simply notice where you can or cannot let go and gently continue loosening unnecessary tension.

Strengthening Inner Attention Through Your Thinking for a Moment of Samadhi

Finally, lie down in savasana. Try to relax your thoughts just as you relaxed your body. Let go of thoughts themselves, such as what you need to do later or something that happened earlier. Do not be concerned about them, and instead, just notice that you are thinking. Stay in this peaceful, relaxed moment, following your own sensations and feelings. You don't need to think about anything else. If your thoughts wander away and you are concerned that you did not do the exercise correctly, gently bring your thoughts back to calmness. Do your best without worrying about it. Pinpoint your thoughts on the present moment and enjoy the peaceful feeling right now. At first, start with 5 minutes and work your way up to 30 minutes. With practice, you will develop a deep sense of calm and well-being, a moment of samadhi.

WORKING WITH RESISTANCE

You may be full of good intentions, but still have difficulty doing these exercises. If you have felt frustrated in your efforts, you may be putting up some resistance. These exercises will help you to overcome any resistance.

Allowing the Play of Thoughts

Perhaps you had difficulty directing your attention to your body because your thinking remained out of control. If you find your thoughts wandering even when you try to direct them, ask yourself: How would I quiet down a group of active children? You might let them be free out on a playground. At first, they will rush around everywhere, but eventually, they will settle down and play quietly. This same principle applies to stilling the thoughts that are racing through your mind. Paradoxically, when you don't resist your instinctive resistance, you often present an opportunity for it to lessen. Then, it will be easier to withdraw your focus when and where you want. The strategy does not always work, but it often does, and so it is worth a try.

Sit quietly and let your thoughts run on, to jump around wherever they want to go, but with one difference: Stay aware of thoughts as they happen, but don't lose touch with the part of you that observes. At first, you will see your thoughts come and go very quickly, like the young child running and jumping around, but in time, just as a child becomes settled, your thoughts will settle down into regular patterns at a manageable speed. Think about each thought is as it appears. Practice this meditation regularly, to reduce the rushing flow of thoughts. Then withdraw from concern about them.

Be Mindful of Your Attention Habits

If you have difficulty doing the pratyahara exercises, delve deeper to notice any hidden assumptions or concerns. Consider the ways you turn your attention to the outer world. For example, are you always planning what you will do next, rehearsing in your mind? Do you have concerns about the past that draw your attention now? Or perhaps you have certain attitudes or beliefs that might be interfering, such as thinking you should always be busy or that relaxation is akin to laziness.

Once you become aware of a habitual preoccupation or attitude, or perhaps an assumption that typically misdirects your attention, adjust your pratyahara practice. For example, if you notice yourself anticipating what you will be doing after your pratyahara session, stop planning, bring your attention back to the moment, and continue to withdraw inward. Or if you continually recount past events, let go of the memories for now. Whenever you realize you are thinking about distractions during pratyahara, gently return to present moment practice. At first, you may struggle, but eventually, extraneous thinking will stop. Then you will be able to enter dharana, the next limb.

TIP: Accept Yourself

Everyone will progress at a distinct pace; so don't judge or chastise yourself. Just observe. If you are nonjudgmental, your mind will open up to you as an ally.

JOURNALING

1. Observe what you experienced with each of these exercises.

2. Journaling can be especially helpful for dealing with resistance. Perform this exercise by writing down each thought you notice.

CHARTING

FIGURE 7.1 Feedback Chart on Pratyahara Meditations

	Ease of practice	Mind wandering	Attention focus	Associated feelings	Associated thoughts
Withdrawing the Senses					
Strengthening Inner Attention Through the Body					
Strengthening Inner Attention Through Your Thinking					
Working with Resistance 1: Allowing the Play of Thoughts					
Working with Resistance 2: Mindful of Attention Habits					

CHAPTER 8

Narrowing Attention (Dharana) to Delve Deeply

There is no limit to the power of the human mind. The more concentrated it is,
the more power is brought to bear on one point. That is the secret.
—Vivekananda, 1953

IN THIS CHAPTER

- Train the ability to narrow your focus while keeping it active
- Practice this skill by actively focusing on an object of interest, on your own breathing, on a sound, and on an action

INTRODUCTION

Now that you have learned how to withdraw your attention, where should it be placed? By means of dharana, you narrow your focus on a single point while keeping it active. Your attention remains there, not as static attention, but as dynamic concentration. Imagine a dog running wildly around. His owner wants to tame him, but how? The owner can tie a leash to the dog's collar and attach this leash to a post in the ground. The dog can roam around the length of the leash, but no farther. Similarly, when you perform dharana meditation, you keep your attention tethered around a topic. Your attention can roam freely around, but it goes nowhere else. Unlike the dog in our metaphor, you *choose* the object of focus and *deliberately* hold your attention on that object. By sincerely making these decisions, you train your attention to become pointed, selective, and concentrated at will. From the sincere commitment and awareness of your choice, your attention naturally flows toward greater discipline. Paradoxically, this act of deliberate attention will prepare you for the development of the ability to automatically allow a meditative union at the later stages of meditation.

The skills of dharana can be especially helpful for quieting uncomfortable feelings or thoughts. By developing the ability to keep your attention fixed on a neutral object or experience, related emotions and thoughts tend to habitually become calm and steady. This steadiness can then be applied to alter problematic emotions and thoughts through their related states of mind.

The Girl Who Turned Her Attention and Situation Around

"I can't stand another minute in that house," shouted Terry about her family. She was a young teenager and lived in a household where her parents were constantly arguing. She felt disturbed and even responsible, since some of their arguments were about her. Her parents were unwilling to join into family therapy, telling us, "Terry is the problem. Do something about her!" As we got to know Terry, we could see that she was in a difficult situation. She was a bright girl, but was struggling to keep her attention on her schoolwork, living as she did in the midst of disturbance at home. She tried to "behave" as her parents put it, but felt like she could never do anything right. She spent a lot of her effort trying to please her parents, worrying about the family, and blaming herself.

We worked on teaching Terry how to draw her attention away from the outer situation by dharana. We started simply, by instructing her to imagine her favorite color and concentrate on it. She liked the feeling of calm she experienced when she kept her attention on the color. She practiced often between sessions. As she developed her skills, she was able to direct her attention where she chose. We asked her about what interested her most in school. She said she loved English. It was her favorite subject. We encouraged her to delve deeper through what she found personally meaningful. She read books by certain authors she liked. She joined a writing club at school and began doing creative writing to express her feelings. In the process, she made new friends who shared her interests. By focusing her attention outward onto school concerns rather than family problems, she began to do better academically and feel happier socially. She also practiced mindfulness, and was able to discern when she was the cause of family disturbances and when she was not. She took responsibility for her own feelings and actions, and learned to stop taking responsibility for her parents' feelings and actions. This helped her put her parents' fighting into a less personally bothersome frame of reference, allowing her to relate better to her surroundings.

In a session with the whole family toward the end of her treatment, her parents expressed gratitude because their daughter seemed happier. They also admitted, "We need to work on our relationship." Terry turned toward them and smiled.

WARMING UP TO DHARANA

Many of our clients have doubted their ability to focus their attention, especially when they were in the midst of disturbance. We have often reassured them that they can do it, as you can now. In fact, you have already practiced dharana many times in your life without realizing it. Begin with the simple action of the next exercise.

Balancing a Cup of Water

Have you ever filled a cup with liquid and carried it carefully over to someone to avoid spilling it? Doing so involves a kind of focus similar to dharana. You must keep all your attention—mind and body—carefully concentrated like a spotlight on the matter at hand. Try this exercise now for the experience.

Fill a cup of water close to the top. Carry it carefully as you walk, without spilling a drop. Move as slowly as you need to in order to prevent the liquid from overflowing. Notice how you must be attuned to the cup while also watching the path as you walk. Your mind and body work together as you move carefully, aware of your every movement in the moment.

PRACTICING DHARANA FOCUS

Any basic activity or thing can be used as an object of concentration, and we will offer opportunities later in the book for applying dharana in creative ways.

Practicing Dharana on an Object

This exercise builds on the meditation tools you developed in Chapter 3, to focus your attention on an object of your choice. To refine your dharana skill even further, pick an object that you find interesting, such as a painting, sculpture, or a graphic you especially like. Place it in clear view. Sit upright in the easy pose and look at the object. Keep your attention on it and notice everything you can: color, texture, shape, size, function, and meaning, if relevant. Do not think about anything else. If your attention wanders away, bring it back to the object. Gradually narrow down the focus until you are just looking at one point on the object. Keep your attention concentrated only on the one point for a few minutes. Next, think carefully about the object. If it is an art object, try to determine its meaning. Does it evoke any emotions? Broaden the focus of the spotlight of your attention and allow yourself to walk all around the object, followed by the spotlight so to speak, viewing it from different perspectives. Begin with just two or three minutes. Gradually increase the time as you become more skilled at shifting focus while in motion. Your ability to follow the flowing changing perspective will improve with continued practice.

Dharana on Breathing

Pranayama breathing may be used with dharana practice. Focus all your attention on breathing while you do it, to develop deep, one-pointed concentration. This leads you into other meditation practices.

For this exercise, sit or lie prone. Most important, allow your breathing passages to be open and relaxed. Close your eyes and turn your attention to your breathing itself. Breathe through your nose, not your mouth. Breathe in and out in a measured way. If it helps, inhale in four counts and exhale in four counts. Use a count that is easy and comfortable for you. Notice the air as it comes in through your nose and then flows down into your lungs and out again. Observe how your chest, diaphragm, stomach, and back move as you breathe. Do not interfere with the natural pattern of breathing. Just relax and breathe comfortably, counting as you concentrate on the process of breathing. If your attention wanders away from breathing, or you lose track, gently bring it back. These skills respond to practice, so be patient.

Dharana on a Mantra

You can focus your attention using any of your senses. An easy way to access your focus is through sound. You probably already become engrossed in music you enjoy; so sound is an effective way to build on what you already know how to do. Mantras are sounds that lend themselves to dharana meditation.

There are many mantras, and we will refer to them throughout this book. The traditional mantra is om. Om is the cosmic vibration of the universe that represents creation and the unity of all things. In the theory, each atom of each molecule of each object in the world vibrates at a certain frequency, which has a corresponding tone. All of these tones, sounded together, make the sound om. Thus, om represents the sound of the universe, when all of its objects are resonating together.

Sit comfortably in the easy pose or in the sitting chair pose, allowing your spine to be straight and your breathing passages to be open. Look at the om picture in Figure 8.1.

Make the sound of om as you would the word home without the h. Then, close your eyes and breathe gently and smoothly for several moments as you relax. When you feel sufficiently calm, slowly inhale, filling your lungs completely. As you exhale, release the sound om. As you get close to the end of your breath, close your lips and vibrate with the "mmmmm" until the sound fades away. Then, gently inhale again and repeat the process. Continue for several minutes, keeping your attention entirely focused on the sound.

Next, imagine yourself making the sound as you breathe in and out, silently. Do this for several minutes as you breathe comfortably.

Now, look at the picture of the word and then close your eyes as you visualize the word. Listen imaginatively and let it become its music. Then contemplate the unity and creation embodied in its music. As you go through the steps, you may feel a resonance like an inert echo. Allow these spiritual feelings to rise up from the mysterious place hidden deep within you. When you feel ready to stop, open your eyes.

FIGURE 8.1 Om Picture

Dharana Focus on Activity

Have you ever found yourself lost in the experience of doing something? Perhaps you were watching a deeply engaging movie, reading an engrossing book, or spending quality time with someone you care about. Where did the time go? With dharana focus on an activity, you can be deliberately, deeply absorbed in the activity of your choice.

Pick something to do that you enjoy. It could be a hobby such as painting, modeling, collecting, or it might be a game or sport you like playing. As you begin to do it, perform it with wholehearted flowing effort. Immerse yourself in the action, making a sincere effort to flow with it, fully engaged. If you are playing tennis, for example, put your whole body into each movement, breathing in coordination. Feel your movements with each stroke. Pay attention to your stance, to the weight of the racket, to the feeling of the ground under your feet, and any other experience that emerges spontaneously as part of your engagement. If you are painting, think only of the paints, the paper, and the brush. Sense your emotions as you paint, noticing the rhythms as your brush moves, the pressure as the tip meets the paper. Be fully attentive to what you are doing as you do it. Let yourself become engrossed with each action: every movement, thought, and/or feeling that goes along with it. If your attention is drawn to something distracting, try to notice. Then, return your focus as soon as you can. Whatever you choose to do, for the time you have set aside for it, do it wholeheartedly and sincerely.

If you are successful with this exercise, you might want to try something more challenging, something you might not enjoy doing or want to do, but need to accomplish. Try to apply the same wholehearted devotion to this more difficult task. Remember that each action matters. Even the most seemingly humble or difficult task has value when done fully and sincerely. By applying your dharana focus, you diminish conflict and increase your one-pointed motivation to do it well. You may find that you can accomplish the task harmoniously, without struggle.

Dharana Focus on the Heart Chakra

Chakras are centers for energy, each symbolizing different aspects of your personality. Focusing on one or another can help to elicit, expand, and deepen these qualities. You will find chakra meditations all through this workbook. Here you can apply dharana focus to your heart chakra, to expand your feelings of love and compassion.

FIGURE 8.2 Heart Chakra

Place your palms lightly over your rib cage, at the level of your heart. This is the location of your heart chakra, the area for love, compassion, and empathy. Close your eyes and sense your heartbeat and the movement of your breath. Now, visualize the air gently circulating around, with each breath in and out, spreading loving kindness everywhere it touches. Visualize the heart chakra imbued with the color green, symbolizing integration with nature, trust in life's flowing energy, emanating from your heart, spreading compassionate feelings through your body and toward others to help create harmony, peace, and prosperity. Breathe quietly for several minutes, feeling your breath, sensing your calm, and expressing your love and compassion for those you care for and care about. In the union with others, you discover samadhi.

JOURNALING

1. What did you experience as you focused on the object (breathing, mantra, activity)?

2. Did you find one exercise easier or more challenging than another?

3. Were you able to hold your attention on the object or did your mind wander?

4. If your mind wandered, when did you notice it, soon after or much later? Were you able to gently bring your attention back to the object?

5. Repeat the exercises and answer these questions again over a period of several weeks. Enter your progress on the chart that follows.

6. Please feel free to note any interesting reflections that you had about your experiences.

CHARTING

FIGURE 8.3 Feedback Chart on Dharana Meditations

	Ease of practice	Mind wandering	Attention focus	Associated feelings	Associated thoughts
Balancing a Cup of Water					
Dharana on Breathing					
Dharana on a Mantra					
Dharana Focus on Activity					
Dharana Focus on the Heart Chakra					

CHAPTER 9

Opening Attention (Dhyana) to Samadhi for Self-Transcendence and Letting Be

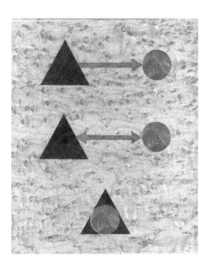

This is the teaching of Yoga. Yoga is the cessation of the turnings of thought.
When thought ceases, the spirit stands in its true identity as observer of the world.
Otherwise, the observer identifies with the turnings of thought.
—Patañjali's Yoga Sutras, 1995

IN THIS CHAPTER

- Let go of your deliberate focus and allow focus to happen spontaneously
- Practice meditations to open attention
- Allow change to take place
- Experience self-transcendence and be unified with your meditation

INTRODUCTION

What is dhyana? Dhyana is that level of meditation where your mind can be still without effort and no longer pushed and pulled by the turnings of thoughts, as Patañjali said. When the turnings of thought cease, you can observe clearly. Like a polished mirror, you reflect everything around you, alert, aware, and at peace within.

You can distinguish dharana meditation in the last chapter from the dhyana meditation in this chapter. They use the mind in two different ways. During dharana, you are aware of what you are meditating on while keeping your attention focused on deliberately meditating. You remain aware during dharana practice, first of the object of meditation and then on yourself as you meditate. You are focusing on the object and deliberately keeping your attention directed to the object of focus. By contrast, when you enter dhyana, you let go of specific thoughts and allow yourself just to become spontaneously aware. You find yourself engrossed in the meditation process itself, without *trying* to do so, just *being* in dhyana. This eventually leads to the experience of merging, unifying, and identifying your consciousness with whatever you are involved in.

At first, you may find yourself exerting effort in applying the therapeutic tools you have developed for reframing troubling thoughts and regulating strong emotions. Then comes a point when you can let go of your absorption in the troubled past, for example, and transcend it. But how can you do this, when the past is all you know, and is the source of your present attitudes? Dhyana meditation allows you to let go and permit something new. You have probably had effortless moments in your life, times when you were so engaged in doing something, so engrossed in your task, that you were completely lost in the activity itself, transcending the sense of yourself as an isolated ego. The difference is between pursuing goals through activity versus just being in the activity. This chapter offers meditation methods to develop this capacity to facilitate your healing journey.

The Man Who Learned That Sleep Comes Best When It's Effortless

Jason had not had a good night's sleep in six years. He was a successful entrepreneur and had a stable, happy relationship with his male partner for many years. So, why, he wondered, couldn't he sleep? He had been to sleep clinics and therapists to no avail. He had a good understanding of his problems and yet, still, no sleep! Now, after so many bad experiences with sleeping, he became apprehensive about falling asleep, which in turn made him less able to sleep.

We worked with meditative hypnosis, a dhyana method to allow his unconscious mind to flow freely. He learned to sensitize himself to the spontaneous natural responsiveness within, so he could let go and let be. We all have a built-in sleep-wake cycle that takes care of itself unless something interferes. Jason learned how to allow this natural system to do its job. As he let go of his worries and allowed himself to relax, nature took its course and his nervous system regained its natural balance. He slept well after the sessions, and with practice at home, he was able to reclaim his built-in capacity to sleep.

NURTURING AN OPEN CONSCIOUSNESS

You have to learn how to push the rock where it wants to go.
—Tanouye Tenshin Roshi in Kushner, 2000

You may find that your thoughts are continually churning, keeping your consciousness full and busy. But with little pushes and nudges in the right direction, you can slow the speed of these thoughts and create spaces between them for contemplation, making way for an open, free consciousness. In doing these meditations, you don't *try* to clear away all your thinking. Rather, you follow the natural flow to stillness. These meditations will lead to a slowing of the relentless stream of thoughts until your consciousness is free from churning from its turnings.

Meditate on the Spaces Between

Notice a time with no immediate responsibilities or obligations coupled with less spontaneous mental activity. Look for such a moment, perhaps at night, just before sleep, during a lunch break, or a time alone when you have nothing pressing to do. At moments like these, you might try to force yourself to do a chore or task. Instead, such a moment can be used as an opportunity to open your attention and find inner quiet.

Let your thoughts drift. Don't do anything and don't think anything about it. Simply sit silently, allowing the experience to emerge and develop. Let your breathing be comfortable and let your body relax. Spend a few minutes permitting your mind to be quiet and explore how expansive that quiet can be. Don't try to discern what it is exactly, but allow this spontaneous tendency to develop. After allowing the naturally occurring quietness, even if only for a brief time, you may find you can deliberately access this mental quiet at other times as well.

Clearing the Mind

Think of your mind as similar to a murky lake that becomes clear when the mud settles to the bottom. The potential for clarity is there in the lake, but the sediment is stirred up. All you need to do is allow everything to settle.

Sit quietly and try not to think about anything. Stay with each moment, without adding any thoughts. Inevitably, thoughts will surface anyway. As a thought occurs, notice it but let it go. Then return to thinking of nothing. Continue to notice any thoughts that come up, but try not to get involved in them. As soon as you can, return to not thinking about anything. Eventually the stream of your thoughts will slow, then become still, leaving you with clear, calm consciousness.

Allowing Open Focus on Breathing

You have practiced deliberate breathing patterns and focus on breathing. Now, without changing your breathing, focus on it as it is right now.

Direct your attention to your breathing and let it remain there, but do so without interfering at all. Continue breathing comfortably and calmly. And as you allow your breathing to be natural, let it find its own rhythm. Your body may relax a bit and your emotions might calm, but don't try to make them do so. Just keep breathing comfortably and allow yourself to be as you are in this moment.

Dhyana Meditation on Music

Do you have a particular piece of music you love? If so, play or listen to it now, and focus your attention on it fully. Enjoy it completely and let yourself move with the beat. Modern researchers use the phrase "being in the groove," (Janata, Tomic, & Haberman, 2012) when you become lost in your favorite music and find that your body spontaneously moves in harmony with it. You might shift side to side, nod your head, tap you hands or feet, or express your feeling in another way. Let yourself "be in the groove," This is a kind of dhyana meditation, natural, spontaneous, without thinking about yourself at all. Just be.

Dhyana in Activity

Have you ever found yourself so engaged in an activity that you did it perfectly, seemingly without effort? The great Zen practitioners call such a moment mushin, a compounding of two terms: *mu* meaning empty and *shin* meaning heart or mind. Some have likened it to samadhi, enlightenment. You can develop this mind-set by doing an activity you have practiced many times. Choose something you enjoy doing, such as a sport or art, that you engage in regularly.

Focus your attention on your chosen activity for several minutes, noticing yourself doing it as you do it. As you continue, let go of trying, and instead, simply allow yourself to move. Don't think about anything, just permit your body to do what it knows how to do. You have practiced often before, so you can trust yourself now.

For example, if you are running, let your legs flow, your breathing coordinate with each step, your arms swing naturally. Forget yourself in action and simply run. Feel yourself flowing along without trying—just running. Or, if you are a painter, let the demands of the painting, with its evolving rhythms and patterns, call forth the movements of the brush. Let the brushstrokes flow from the brush as your hand and arm move. Through immersion in the activity, you become one with it, and your movements are the natural expression. Forget yourself in creating, and just create. Let your mind be clear and follow the flow as it evolves. When finished, stop, and be quiet for a moment with a clear, calm mind.

BRINGING IT ALL TOGETHER: SAMYAMA

All the steps you have taken so far lead to samyama, that is, "holding together" or "binding." Unifying breathing, body posture, and focus puts you on the path. Then withdrawing your attention and keeping it focused on something takes you to the point where meditation (dhyana) will happen spontaneously, resulting in samadhi. As you become fully absorbed in the moment, you develop intuitive understanding and insight into whatever you are focusing on.

Set aside a longer period of time for meditation. Sit quietly and turn your attention somewhere, either to an outer object or within. Turn your attention gently there, but don't force it to go there. During this process, while you sit quietly, you will have moments where something happens, if you can allow it. You may feel a tranquil meditative state sweep over you. The boundary between you as the person meditating and the process of meditating loses its meaning. At first, you may just have a fleeting moment, but with practice, the experience will last longer. Let go of your conscious, rational thoughts and allow the spontaneous expression of your unconscious and intuitive capacities. This might be difficult at first. But as you continue to invite openness, it will become effortless. Let it happen and enjoy the experience!

JOURNALING

1. Make a journal entry after each exercise. Note what you have experienced.

2. Did you feel as if you needed to keep control or could you allow your experience to unfold?

3. If you were able to let go, describe what you felt. Was it comfortable or uncomfortable, and in what way?

4. Experiment with dhyana journaling. Just start writing whatever comes to mind and let it be expressed. Then let writing flow without a goal. Just express yourself. Fine-tune it later.

CHAPTER 10

Mindfulness for Nonjudgmental Acceptance, Presence, and Awareness

Wherever your attention alights, at this very point, experience.
—Malini Vijaya Tantra

IN THIS CHAPTER

- Apply suspending judgment
- Learn how to accept things as they are
- Practice mindfulness on all levels—physical, emotional, mental, and spiritual
- Bring it all together for mindfulness moment-by-moment

INTRODUCTION

Yoga breathing, postures, and meditative focus shape you every day and in every way. Bringing your mind fully into each present moment, each posture, and each breath enhances yoga practice and facilitates therapeutic work. Mindfulness training begins by suspending judgment, allowing you to widen the scope of your experience. Learning to develop nonjudgmental awareness and acceptance is extremely helpful for therapeutic progress. Mindfulness, with its nonjudgmental awareness and acceptance is a skill that takes practice. So, doing the mindfulness exercises in this chapter is important for building your skills. You can break the process down into various components, and you will practice mindfulness of the body, emotions, thoughts, and the thinking process to build your skills. Eventually, it will all come together, and what began as a deliberate effort will become a natural and spontaneous adjustment to life, awake and aware, without worrying and evaluating, simply being present.

The Man Who Went from "Beware" to "Be Aware"

Roger was tough. His biceps showed through his close fitting T-shirt, and his short-cropped hair revealed a menacing tattoo on his forehead. His eyes riveted through you, and when he spoke, he sounded like a series of loud growls. He was referred to therapy because of his aggressive behavior. Although therapy was not his idea, he said, "I don't mind being here because I'm f. . .ing tired of getting locked up!" (He generously sprinkled expletives throughout his speech. We leave it to the reader to fill those in.) "I don't know how it happens. I'm cool! The only reason I get in fights is that people are such idiots!"

We taught him mindfulness, so that he could learn to observe his experience and suspend judgment. He practiced in the office and at first observed surface things, "I notice I'm sitting. I am aware of you looking at me." We asked him to notice his sensations and body experience. "I feel fine," was his first response. We encouraged him to follow his sensations, feelings, and thoughts for two or three minutes at different times during the week, and he agreed to do it. When he returned, he told us that as he did it more often, he began noticing things he usually overlooked. He listened to people's voices as they were talking with him. He heard his own voice, and it sounded louder and harsher than other people's voices. He became aware of how people around him acted afraid. And he observed that when people spoke to him, he felt irritated by certain voice tones he heard, for no real reason. As we discussed his observations each week, he began to recognize that his irritation was actually fueled by his own inner issues. By observing and listening closely, he noticed that he was feeling angry much of the time. His anger sensitized him, and he attributed annoyed meanings to overtones he heard in other's voices that they were not intending. With this realization, he was able to work on the source of the anger within him, and he stopped perceiving annoyance in others. Instead of radiating *beware*, his way became a more peaceful one: *to be aware.*

SUSPENDING JUDGMENT; OPENING TO ACCEPTANCE

Mindfulness offers a distinct approach for observing actions, thoughts, and feelings. But when you look more deeply, you may not always like what you see. You might feel like passing judgment on yourself or others before you really understand. Keep in mind that negative judgments about what you are experiencing narrow down what you notice, leading you to miss key aspects. Mindful awareness involves being objective—simply looking and sensing what is really there. Like a scientist who is gathering data, don't jump to conclusions or use the new information you gain to form biased opinions. Instead, be objective. For the purposes of mindful awareness, suspend your judgments and simply let the experience unfold. Trust the process and you will develop an open mind. Be aware.

Mindfulness of Body: Begin by Suspending Judgment About Your Body

To begin suspending judgment, notice details of your physical experience. Accept the bad along with the good, and cultivate detachment.

Survey yourself from head to toe and recognize all your different parts. Describe each part to yourself. For example, notice your hair—its color, texture, style—your eyes, etc. But stay factual. You might observe that your hair is a certain color or straight or curly or long or short. Perhaps you see qualities that you never quite noticed before. Don't add evaluations, such as my hair is too dark or too curly. Simply observe your hair as it is, dark and curly.

If you discover something about yourself that you don't like, take note of it. Know that you are noticing something you don't like. You may decide this quality should eventually be changed, but for the moment, observe the experience you are having: "wanting change." What are the qualities of "wanting change?" Are there any emotions that go with it? Are there any body sensations? Notice that you want change, without self-criticism. Observe it, note the feeling that you want to change, and accept it as another experience. If you begin to evaluate it as a negative quality, notice that you are doing so. Whenever you can simply observe, you will find that perception opens. Thus, this is a two-part exercise in that you are, first, allowing your experience to flow, but then you are also noticing it as it occurs. Let yourself be aware of the moment and in the moment. Keep your observations clear and descriptive. Learn to accept your experience of yourself, without making comparisons or criticisms to something outside of this moment. Then you will be able to appreciate the full range of experiencing, just as it is. And you will be able to choose how to respond.

MINDFUL PRACTICES

Mindfulness can be practiced in many ways. Here are some variations to help you become aware of your body, emotions, and thinking processes.

Body Mindfulness: Noticing Body Sensations

Sit down in a chair or choose one of the sitting positions, and turn your attention to your body. Begin by noticing your body sensations as they are occurring. Perhaps you might sense your skin temperature or the softness of the chair you are sitting on, or possibly a tight muscle or relaxed breathing. Let your attention move moment-by-moment as you become aware of one sensation or another. As each moment is new, you will find that the next moment is not necessarily an exact replica of the last. Follow the flow of your sensory experiencing for several minutes.

Remember, don't pass judgments on your experience. If you find yourself saying, "I like this sensation," or, "I hate that one," notice that you are making a judgment, and if you can, set it aside. Instead, experience the sensation and accept it just as it is.

Variations of Body Mindfulness

Notice your sensations when you are in different body positions (standing, sitting, or lying prone). When you first wake up in the morning, begin by taking a moment to feel your body as you lie in bed. Once you get up, pay attention to how you sit up, step onto the floor, and slowly stand up. Take note of your body positions whenever you have a chance throughout your day. You can even extend being mindful of your body while you walk. Wherever you find yourself, as you go about your day, take a moment to notice your physical sensations.

Mindful Breathing

Many people find that paying attention to breathing is one of the easiest ways to begin the process of becoming more aware. Having worked with breathing in Chapter 5, you will already have built some skills. You may find mindful breathing a natural way to bring yourself into the practice of mindfulness. Perform this exercise regularly.

Sit on a small pillow on the floor and cross your legs. If you have difficulty sitting on the floor, please feel free to sit in a chair. Let your hands rest comfortably on your legs. Keep your back relatively straight so that your breathing passages are free and unrestricted. Close your eyes and breathe normally.

Notice as you bring the air in through your nose. Feel the air in your nasal passages and sense the movement in your chest and diaphragm. Stay with the sensation as the air travels into your lungs. Next, follow the air as it moves out. Note how your diaphragm pushes down as the air travels up and out through your nasal passages. Feel the sensation of air pushing out as it leaves your nose. Now follow the next breath in the same way. You will notice slight variations, because each moment is new and each breath is a new breath. And you will recognize that breathing involves many different sensations.

Continue breathing mindfully for several minutes. If you catch your attention drifting away from your breathing, gently bring it back. Follow your breathing, just as it is. You may feel yourself calming as you breathe and remain aware of your breath. The sense of inner peace this engenders will become a resource.

Mindful of Emotions

You can extend mindfulness to your emotions by turning your attention to what you are feeling right now.

To start the process, sit down for a moment and close your eyes. Turn your attention inward and notice what you are feeling. Perhaps you feel calm as you sit quietly. Follow the feeling and notice if it changes. Perhaps now you feel happy or excited about what you are doing. Then, as you continue to pay attention, does your emotion change again? Let yourself become curious and explore each feeling as it arises. Sense the location of the feeling in your body, how it changes over time, and what it becomes as you stay attuned to it and aware of it.

Don't judge whether each feeling is good or bad, or whether you like it or don't like it. Instead, observe, accepting each feeling just as it is. You are merely gathering information that will be helpful to you on your mindful journey. By observing your feelings, even the ones you might not like, you will learn more about yourself. And as you eliminate adverse reactions to a negative feeling, you will become more accepting of what is, as it is, and be more able to move on to the next feeling.

Be Mindful During a Strong Emotion

Mindfulness can be helpful when you are having a very strong emotion that takes over and fills you with urgency. If this occurs, choose to observe what you are feeling for a specific length of time, for example, 5 minutes. Take note of the sensations, the thoughts that go with the emotion, any impulses to act, and anything else that comes into your awareness. But remember, don't judge it as awful or wonderful—just notice it as you sit quietly. Without trying to stop what you are feeling, notice how the emotion gradually changes or is transformed over time. Typically, as you pay attention to troubling emotions mindfully, at first they fill your mind, and then they become less severe. So, if you mindfully experience a negative emotion, the feeling will eventually lose its intensity, while you will increasingly find yourself feeling calm. Take note of how you experience change in your body sensations as well. Notice that your cheeks cool down, the uncomfortable feeling in your stomach goes away, and perhaps your tense muscles loosen. As pointed out, meditation has a moderating influence on emotions, making them easier to cope with. So stay with the emotion if you can, and be alert and aware of each changing moment. Trust that time will bring relief.

Mindful of Thinking

Through mindful awareness, you can observe the typical thinking processes that seem to fill each moment, and begin to recognize that you have an ongoing series of ever-changing thoughts. And with this awareness comes greater clarity, balance, and calm.

Become Mindfully Aware of Thoughts

Being mindful of your thoughts begins by first recognizing what you are thinking in the moment. Sit quietly and close your eyes. Notice what you are thinking as you think it. Follow the flow of your thoughts. Imagine you are sitting on the bank of a river, watching leaves and twigs flow by. Don't jump into the river but stay back on the shore, watching. Keep observing and letting each thought drift past. If you find yourself drifting downstream with a thought, climb back on shore and resume observing.

Mindful of the Flow of Thoughts

Now, instead of focusing on what you are thinking, move your attention to the flow itself. Do the thoughts flow by quickly or do they move slowly.

How does a thought come into your mind? Does it suddenly appear, seeming to come from nowhere, or does it drift in slowly and gradually? Notice, too, how the thought leaves. Does it disappear suddenly as you move on to another thought, or does it fade away gradually as another thought arises? Are there spaces between thoughts or do they occur one after the other?

Continue attending to the flow of thoughts without getting caught up in any particular thought. Don't make any judgments about it. Simply accept your thinking processes just as they are. Notice any changes that might occur as you remain mindfully attuned to your thoughts.

BRINGING IT ALL TOGETHER

Body sensations, feelings, and thoughts are present in every moment. Bring your mindfulness practice together and feel aware and in touch with what you are experiencing in the moment.

Mindful in the Moment

Bring all the ways of being mindful to the present moment. Pay close attention to whatever you are experiencing right now. Scan through your body and notice any sensations. Observe your feelings and notice any thoughts you might be having. As you become centered in the moment, be present.

Your experience transforms moment-by-moment. Whenever possible, turn your attention to your moment-by-moment experience. Be in touch mindfully as often as possible. In time, mindfulness will become habitual and natural.

Minute Mindfulness in Action

Pick a short activity that you perform every day, such as brushing your teeth. Make a conscious effort to attend to it mindfully, from beginning to end. Before beginning, stop for a few seconds and breathe with awareness of each breath in and out. Then begin the activity: Notice the taste of the toothpaste, the temperature of the water, and the sensation of the toothbrush on your teeth. Feel your arm as it moves, and notice your body position at the sink. When you have finished, take a few seconds to pay attention to the sensations of your mouth and face.

Another activity that lends itself well to minute mindfulness is taking a shower or a bath. Any brief activity that you do regularly can be a good place to start. Continue to bring mindfulness more and more into each day by attending to other short activities.

JOURNALING

1. Keep a journal of your mindfulness practice. Practice all the exercises in this chapter, writing what you experience as you experience it.

2. Spend a set amount of time each day, perhaps at different times of the day, writing in your mindful journal.

3. Record your moment-by-moment experience without evaluation or judgment.
   a. When you do this exercise, the writing will be spontaneous and almost unconscious.
   b. Don't stop to think back about a feeling or emotion, just stay in the moment. Later, you might want to read what you wrote.
   c. Remember, don't judge your journal entry.
   d. Accept each mindful entry as it is. You will grow through the process!

Part III

Applying Yoga and Mindfulness

Just continue in your calm, ordinary practice, and your character will be built up.
—Shunryu Suzuki, 1979

IN PART III

- Learn yoga and mindfulness protocols specifically designed to treat common psychological problems:
  - ☐ Lessen stress
  - ☐ Alleviate anxiety
  - ☐ Overcome trauma
  - ☐ Ease depression
  - ☐ Conquer addiction
  - ☐ Develop well-being

Yoga and mindfulness practices are well suited to overcoming psychological problems. Part III guides you in working with difficulties to bring about a healthier and happier way of living. We encourage you to do the exercises and allow yourself to feel the effects as they take hold over time. You will find one chapter for each of the problems covered: stress, anxiety, trauma, depression, and substance abuse. We encourage you to practice the exercises from all the chapters and apply them creatively for your benefit.

CHAPTER 11

Handling Stress and Facilitating Optimal Coping

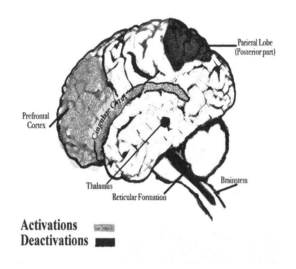

The mind of the perfect person is like a mirror.
It does not lean forward or backward in its response to things.
—Chan, 1963

IN THIS CHAPTER

- Review of how stress manifests in the nervous system
- Discover how yoga and mindfulness help calm the stress pathway
- Practice bottom-up and top-down methods to shift the stress pathway back to normal
- Monitor stress mindfully with charts

INTRODUCTION

According to the American Psychological Association, most mental disorders are stressful, placing extra demands on the nervous system (American Psychological Association, 2008). The response to stress is built into the nervous system in what is known as the fear/stress pathway. When functioning well, this pathway helps to alert you and protect you from threats. You can learn to manage this natural nervous system pathway and balance your responses so that the reaction works to your benefit. Yoga and mindfulness offer tangible tools known to influence the brain's fear/stress pathway. You can learn to listen to your nervous system signals, reduce your stress response when it is overly extreme, and manage life situations better. In addition, addressing stressful situations well will have a healing influence on other problems you might want to change.

The Woman Who Learned to Handle Pressure Without Stress

Diane was working excessively hard. She had an important position at an advertising firm that involved her traveling most weeks. Her appearance suggested authority, with her tailored suit and perfectly coiffed hair. She sat upright with crossed-legs and spoke with confidence. As an executive who was in charge of putting together ideas and presenting them to potential customers, she carried a heavy weight of responsibility. As a result, she often had to work long into the night to put the final touches on the next day's presentation. One way she tried to alleviate her stress was by eating at expensive restaurants and shopping for designer clothes. At first, she felt justified in these indulgences, since she was working so hard. But when her expensive clothes became too tight from overindulging in food, she felt upset. She tried one extreme diet after another, sustaining a strict regime for only a few days or weeks. Her roller coaster of dieting and binging sapped her energy, and she told us, "I feel ragged! I'm losing my edge!"

We introduced Diane to yoga and mindfulness to help her rediscover her natural balance, working both bottom-up and top-down. She practiced the sun salutation (Surya Namascara) routine described in this chapter each morning before breakfast to initiate bottom-up change in her nervous system. She found that she felt calmer after she did it. In time, she was able to sustain calm longer into the day. She liked that she could perform the postures in her hotel room and that her muscles were becoming toned. She learned mindfulness, and practiced at night. As she meditated regularly, she got in touch with her deeper motivations. She realized that her love of fine clothes and gourmet food was actually an appreciation for beauty and art. We encouraged her to strengthen this higher calling (recall the niyama, ishvara pranidhana, to seek higher values). At first, she made it a practice to add a short visit to a museum or important landmark on each trip. As she exposed herself more to art, she stirred her inner art spirit. She started adding an artistic touch to her work, inspiring others with her creative presentations. Meditating regularly, practicing yoga postures, and satisfying her higher aesthetic sense, she found a healthy balance and could handle pressures without undue stress. Soon she enjoyed her work more and indulged her gourmet tastes in moderation.

STRESS AND YOUR NERVOUS SYSTEM

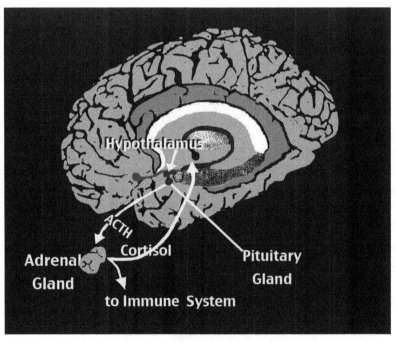

FIGURE 11.1 HPA Fear/Stress Pathway

Your nervous system has a built-in capacity to detect and respond to anything that threatens you. Here's how it works:

- Activation of the hypothalamus-pituitary-adrenal (HPA) fear pathway

    - When you face something that you perceive as a threat, your amygdala (the gateway for processing emotions) is alerted and sends a signal to the endocrine system through the hypothalamus (which regulates homeostasis and acts quickly) and to the pituitary and adrenal glands.

    - This group of organs function together.

- Hormones and neurotransmitters involved

    - This fear pathway regulates how your body responds to a threat by modulating the secretion of hormones and neurotransmitters that help to keep your body in balance. Corticotrophin-releasing hormone from the hypothalamus (CRH) signals the adrenocorticotropic hormone from the pituitary (ACTH) and cortisol from the adrenal glands, which in turn signal for activation. The heart rate increases and palms sweat, while breathing rate increases and becomes shallower.

    - You also have hormones and neurotransmitters that decrease the reaction when the danger has passed or the balance of hormones has been lost. Glucocorticoids are released and fed back into the brain, which signals the pituitary to slow down the synthesis of CRH and ACTH, reducing cortisol.

- Autonomic nervous system involvement

    - Your autonomic nervous system is well equipped to respond rapidly to traumatic, frightening, or dangerous events when it receives signals from the HPA fear pathway.
        - The two branches of the autonomic nervous system work together to help you meet each situation well.
        - The sympathetic nervous system activates you to take necessary action, such as making your heart pump faster.
        - The parasympathetic nervous system inhibits action, such as slowing your heart rate after danger has passed.

- The fear pathway is protective

    - The fear pathway protects you from danger by making it possible for you to respond quickly. This circular process of activation and deactivation is usually kept in balance with your real-life situations.

- When the fear pathway remains activated

    - The fear pathway is not only activated by an immediate threat but also from remembering a past threat. You might continue to sustain the reaction by remembering a past threat vividly, as if you are still in the threatening situation. This occurs because the hippocampus, where memories are stored, is closely linked to the amygdala.

- How the activated fear pathway becomes a stress pathway

    - This normal, protective fear pathway transforms into a stress pathway by remaining activated without flowing back to a resting state. When your nervous system stays in an over-activated state, it can put a strain on your mind, brain, and body, similar to how revving your car at high rpms is hard on the engine. When you are under stress, your thinking processes become somewhat disrupted, and you feel tired and nervous. You may also have difficulty sleeping, and eat too much or too little.

In numerous studies, yoga and mindfulness have been found to lower the activation of the nervous system and restore balance.

CHARTING YOUR STRESS PATTERN

You may have lost awareness of your stress response, particularly if it has been sustained over a long period. You can, however, learn to recognize some of the signs of your stress pattern that occur when your stress pathway remains activated. Use the stress symptom checklists here to track the changes that occur in your body, emotions, and behavior. Check off the typical symptoms that you notice when you are stressed. Then you can anticipate the onset. When you observe that you have entered your stress pattern, practice the exercises in this chapter to help shift to a healthier balance.

FIGURE 11.2 Chart Your Stress Reaction

PHYSICAL SYMPTOMS CHECKLIST				
	How often	How intense	How bothered	Observations
Dry mouth				
Excessive sweating				
Frequent Illnesses				
Gastrointestinal problems				
Grinding your teeth				
Headache				
Increased blood pressure				
Pounding heart				
Stiff neck or sore lower back				

EMOTIONAL SYMPTOM CHECKLIST				
	How often	How intense	How bothered	Observations
Anxiety				
Chronic fatigue				
Easily startled				
Impulsiveness				
Difficulty concentrating				
Irritability				
Trouble remembering things				

BEHAVIORAL SYMPTOM CHECKLIST				
	How often	How intense	How bothered	Observations
Crying				
Change in your eating habits				
Impatience				
Trouble communicating				
Avoiding friends and family				
Increased use of drugs, alcohol, or tobacco				

REBALANCING THE FEAR/STRESS PATHWAY

You can calm your nervous system bottom up, by rebalancing and calming your body. You can also think about the stressors that you face, influencing the reaction top down. We have found that working on stress both top down and bottom up has a more powerful effect. The exercises that follow offer bottom-up and top-down processing methods to help you calm a chronically over-activated stress pathway and find a balance that will help you meet your demands optimally.

WORKING FROM THE BOTTOM UP

Bottom-up change can be initiated through a variety of postures and breathing exercises. When initiating a change to your nervous system, allow some time to feel the effects. Make these exercises a regular part of your routine, and you will eventually sustain deeper calm and comfort.

Bottom-up Calming with the Sun Salutation

The sun gives its energy to the world, and similarly, the sun salutation is believed to energize the entire body. The dynamic, balanced movements reach from head to toe, with forward and backward bending movements. Breathing is combined with the movements to help you develop control and be calm. This series can help you lose weight, massage your digestive system, and regulate circulation. Regular practice will lead to feelings of well-being.

TIP: Keep your mind focused on your movements and your breathing. Relax any unnecessarily tense areas to allow your body to move gently back and forth, without forcing a movement to a position farther than is comfortable. Don't make yourself take deep breaths, just breathe comfortably as you move. Be patient and persistent for the best results. With breath and movement united, you will free the flow of energy to help you find calm and balance.

Performing the Sun Salutation

The sun salutation is performed in slow, continuous motion. You can repeat the entire series several times, up to ten times each day, but two to three times is usual, especially if you do it daily.

Breathing should be coordinated with each move in the following way: Breathe in when you stretch back or arch. Breathe out when you bend forward or contract inward. Make your breaths and your movements slow and continuous. As you learn to pay attention to what you are doing and synchronize your breathing with your movements, you will experience a union of mind and body that can be uplifting. Allow yourself to enjoy this experience.

Before you begin, warm up for several minutes with a few gentle stretches and arm swings, and by raising and lowering your legs. Once your body feels limbered and relaxed, begin performing the sun salutation.

1. *Opening Position: Stand straight in the mountain pose, with your feet together, chest lifted, shoulders square, and neck lengthened. Bend your elbows and hold the palms of your hands together, thumbs touching, at the center of your chest. Keep your weight evenly distributed between your two feet. Close your eyes and breathe in and out several times, centering yourself in your body experience as you stand quietly.*

2. *Upright Arch Open your eyes and inhale as you stretch your arms up over your head, palms facing each other. Arch back as you push your hips out, keeping your legs straight. Gently relax your neck back. Begin to arch from your upper back rather than the lower back. Arch slowly and carefully.*

FIGURE 11.3 Sun Salutation Opener

FIGURE 11.4 Upward Arch

3. *Forward Bend: Exhale as you slowly bend forward, keeping your arms extended. Move your arms and upper body downward, bending at the waist, toward the floor. Keep your back straight for as long as possible as you go down. Let your neck relax and your head hang down. Bring your fingertips down to your toes and bend your knees slightly if needed. Hold briefly as you relax fully into the forward stretch.*

FIGURE 11.5a Forward Bend A *and* **11.5b** Forward Bend B

4. *Lunging Arch: Inhale as you extend your left leg back approximately four feet behind your right, allowing your left knee to rest on the floor. Your right foot rests flat on the floor with your knee bent. Let your hands rest on the floor at your sides to steady this motion. Then, raise your arms up overhead, arch your back and look up toward the sun. If you feel unstable in your balance, keep your hands on the floor at your sides as you arch. Hold briefly, allowing your upper body to stretch backward as much as is comfortable.*

FIGURE 11.6 Lunge

5. *Dog Pose: Exhaling, bring your left foot back next to the right and perform the dog pose. Lift your hips up as high as you can as you place your hands, palms down on the floor extended out in front of you. Expand your chest as you relax your neck and look down between your hands. Push your heels toward the floor, allowing a gentle stretch.*

FIGURE 11.7 Downward Dog

6. *Cobra Stretch: Lower yourself face down to the floor and inhale as you perform the cobra pose, arching and drawing your upper body slowly up, vertebrae by vertebrae, beginning at your lower back and moving upward. As you get to the neck area, allow your head to arch back slowly until you achieve a full upper body stretch.*

FIGURE 11.8 Cobra

7. *Now you are halfway through the series of movements. The second half of the sun salutation involves repeating all the same motions on the opposite side. (if you began with your right leg forward and your left leg extended back, now bring your left foot forward and extend your right leg back.) Following the cobra pose, perform the dog pose as you exhale. Then lunge back with your right leg as you inhale and smoothly arch back with your upper body. Exhale as you bring your right leg back to your left and lift your hips up as you bend your upper body down, bringing your head toward your knees. Straighten your upper body up and lift your arms overhead to stretch backward as you inhale. End as you began, with your arms returning to the position at your chest, palms and thumbs touching. Pause, close your eyes, and pay attention to your feelings as you sense the effects of the sun salutation. Meditate for a moment in this position, and then begin again.*

Bottom Up: Soft Breathing Meditation

The breath is a direct link to the emotions and the nervous system, so it can be used as a resource for calming. This classic breathing exercise helps to gently soften each breath, thereby setting in motion a calmer mind and body. Perform this exercise at different times throughout the day and evening when in the midst of stress to offer yourself an oasis of relaxation and calm. Your nervous system eventually responds naturally with a shift to a more comfortable balance.

Sit comfortably with your legs crossed on a pillow on the floor. Or, if you prefer a chair, sit in an upright chair letting your feet rest flat on the floor. In either position, keep your back relatively straight so that your breathing passages are unobstructed. Take a few minutes to focus on breathing, either listening to your breath or counting the breaths as described in Chapter 5. When your attention is fairly well focused on breathing, soften your breath. Draw air in gently and smoothly, not too fast or too slow, and then let it softly and smoothly out. There is no need to force or hold your breath. Instead, just breathe gently and comfortably. Your breathing will be natural and light, but slightly slower. Keep your attention focused on your breathing and sustain this for several minutes, working up to 10 to 15 minutes.

Savasana or Crocodile Relaxation

Taking time to deliberately relax is a helpful component of a stress-reducing regimen. We encourage you to take a periodic break to lie down either in savasana (on your back) or crocodile (on your belly). Refer to the instructions for "Prone Pose, Savasana" and "Crocodile Pose, Makarasana" in Chapter 6, pages 56-57, for the position. As you lie comfortably, allow your breathing to be soft and steady. Notice the surface you are lying on and how your body meets this surface. If you notice you are holding your body away from the surface, try to let go as if sinking into it or floating lightly over it. You may notice tension in your neck, back, shoulders, or perhaps arms or legs. If so, can you allow these muscles to relax?

Pratyahara: Take a Short Vacation from Stress

Pratyahara is the discipline of withdrawing your senses from the outer world. See Chapter 7 for additional pratyahara exercises. You can use any of these exercises to take a short vacation from a stressful situation, allowing your nervous system an opportunity to rest and restore. Practice this meditation often, for short periods—even one minute will do—and you might find that you can handle stress more easily and comfortably.

Lie down in the savasana pose. Withdraw your attention from your outer surroundings as much as possible. Do not, for example, listen to the sounds of traffic outside. Instead, turn your attention inward. Begin by turning your attention to your muscles. Notice where they feel tense and where they feel relaxed. If you are able, let go of any tensions that you might not need. Breathe comfortably and allow any relaxation that can occur. Now, try to relax your thoughts just as you relax your body. Without forcing thoughts to relax, simply let any irrelevant thoughts go and stay with this peaceful, relaxed moment. If you find yourself thinking about your stressful situation, remind yourself that right now you are turning inward rather than outward. And in this quiet moment, there doesn't need to be stress, since you are resting quietly. Bring your attention back to your muscles, your breathing, and the calm moment now. You do not need to think about anything outside, just your own inner calm as it develops now. If you notice your thoughts wandering, gently bring them back to this calm moment as soon as you can. Continue focusing inwardly. Start with a very short time, especially if you feel pressured. Sustain this meditation for longer periods as you develop more skill, allowing periods of relief for your mind, brain, and body.

TOP-DOWN CHANGE USING MINDFULNESS

Mindfulness has a dual effect of calming the lower areas in the brainstem while simultaneously activating the attentional areas of your prefrontal cortex. Practice mindfulness meditation daily. Use the methods in Chapter 10, beginning with mindfulness of body, feelings, and thoughts. Take another step back to notice the flow of experiencing as well. Do you feel bombarded with experiences? Often when people are stressed, they feel overwhelmed by an intensity of stimuli. Recall that with mindful observing, you simply notice the qualities of sensations, thoughts, and feelings, just as they are. As you follow your experience moment-by-moment, also observe how it changes throughout the meditation session. You may find that thoughts become clear, emotions steady, and sensations ease. You may also discover that you have resistance to implementing the skills, leading to defenses that turn off self-awareness. Take note of them. You can learn a lot from your resistant reactions. Make mindfulness a regular practice and you will initiate a change in your way of responding to stress.

Fostering a Nonjudgmental Attitude Toward Stress

It has become a cultural mantra to lament about the stressful pace of life. How many times have you complained about how stressed you are? But by emphasizing how bad, hard, or painful your stress is, you inadvertently make it worse! You will find a distinct benefit from altering your judgmental thinking. This series of meditations will help you to become mindfully aware of your judgments as you make them, and then guide you in changing them.

Notice Your Judgments

Begin by sitting comfortably and relaxing for a minute. Now, take a step back from your usual thoughts about your stress level to notice what you are telling yourself. Are you telling yourself negative things such as "I'm really stressed!" or "How awful this situation is!" or "Other people are bothering me, and shouldn't!"? Be mindful of whatever you are thinking about. You may find it easier to notice by saying to yourself, "Now I am aware of thinking this; now I am thinking that. . ." But when you tell yourself how bad things are, you are making an evaluation. Each judgment, whether accurate or not, is not the stress itself. These judgments remove you from your experience in this moment and add to your discomfort. Observe the judgment within the thought. Mindfully recognizing when you are adding to your discomfort with negative judgments will lower your stress.

Mindful of Reactions to Judgments

Now, how do you react to your judgmental assessments of yourself? Taking a moment to reflect inwardly on what you sense, feel, and think immediately after making a judgment will help you to answer this question. Perform this exercise whenever you find yourself judging something or someone.

Mindfully notice any physical sensations, emotions, or thoughts you might be having immediately following any judgments that you make. For example, if you judged that stress is awful and you can't stand it, do you feel an evoked sensation such as tightness in a muscle, a quickening of your breathing, or a stab of anxiety? Continue in this way for several minutes, noticing your judgments and any reactions to them. If you detect a pattern of worry or anxiety during the day, look for a judgmental thought behind it. When you feel that you have become aware of your judgments and your reactions to them, move on to the next exercise.

Challenge Your Judgments

You probably have begun to notice how your judgments elicit uncomfortable reactions. This meditation will show you how to let go of your negative thought habits so that you can open the way for something better.

Sit comfortably for a moment and allow yourself to relax. We invite you to think differently for a moment. Have you ever considered that sometimes stress may serve an important purpose? For example, higher education is worthwhile, but most students will agree that the tests and papers are stressful. People sometimes feel stressed while planning a wedding, but once it's all finished, most people will remember the wedding experience as deeply meaningful. And there are many reports of ordinary people who act heroically during a disaster, often gaining more self-confidence from having met a stressful situation courageously. Is there any way that you can construe your stressful situation as a challenge that may help you to transcend your limits or to grow as a person?

Inviting a More Mature Reaction

Is there a more compassionate way to view your situation? Begin by reflecting on your judgmental response, and ask inwardly, "Does this assessment bring about harmony, peaceful resolution, and make me more able to cope? Or does this judgment bring disharmony, discomfort, and lessen my ability to cope?" Empathize with the other person's feelings and situation, not limited by your personal point of view, but instead, put yourself in the other person's shoes. Ask yourself, "How could I be more compassionate and understanding?" Notice your experiencing now, as you consider a more sympathetic and caring perspective. You may find your discomfort eases and new options open up to you.

Building on Your Strengths

Vividly imagine taking appropriate action toward what you can realistically influence. For example, if you worry that you can't handle something, imagine that you can handle a small aspect of it well. Extend your gaze to include more of the situation, and then picture yourself doing your best, even though you may face obstacles. See yourself handling this stressful event calmly and competently. Be patient as you relax into the experience and wait for your response. Don't do anything to force it to happen. Simply let the scene unfold. Then, allow the image to become clearer, enlisting all your senses.

CHARTING

As you perform the different exercises in this chapter, you will activate alterations in your nervous system response. Reflect on what you sensed, felt, and thought following the different types of yoga and mindfulness practices.

FIGURE 11.9 Chart Your Stress Reduction Experience

	Felt calmer	Less symptoms	Felt happier	Experienced well-being	More optimistic
Following Yamas and Niyamas Practice					
Following Breathing Meditations					
Following Posture Practice					
Following Mindfulness Meditations					
Overall Experience					

CHAPTER 12

Lowering Anxiety and Developing Inner Calm

For a peaceful meditation, we need not go to the mountains and streams.
When thoughts are quieted down, fire itself is cool and refreshing.
—Suzuki, 1973

IN THIS CHAPTER

- Distinguish the different forms of anxiety
- Examine the anxious brain
- Engage your whole being: mind, body, and spirit
- Calm your nervous system with postures, breathing, and meditation
- Enlist mindful attention
- Work through by building understanding, courage, and acceptance

INTRODUCTION

If you are feeling anxious, you have probably noticed that anxiety has many different effects on you. You might have nervous feelings, thoughts, and uncomfortable sensations in your body as well. In fact, anxiety does influence all of these levels. And so, it makes sense to overcome anxiety by enlisting every resource you have, using your mind, body, and spirit. Yoga and mindfulness are well suited for lowering anxiety, since these practices work on all these different levels together, to alter the whole mind-brain-body system in positive ways. A great deal of research shows how effective yoga and mindfulness are for anxiety. In our recent book, *Meditation and Yoga in Psychotherapy*, we recount many of the scientific studies that use yoga to treat anxiety (Simpkins, 2010), and in *Zen Meditation in Psychotherapy*, we describe mindfulness research (Simpkins, 2011). You can be confident when using yoga and mindfulness to alleviate anxiety.

Approach the exercises in this chapter with patience. Remember that it takes time to alter an entrenched pattern. Even drug therapies can take several weeks before beginning to have an effect. You may not feel the results of yoga and mindfulness immediately. The effects are gradual. Expect to feel relief over time, as your turbid pattern of anxiety dissolves in the clear waters of meditation.

The Girl Who Found Stillness Without Having to Sit Still

Teresa was in her senior year at college. She had been a top student and had started applying to graduate school. But this year, she was having trouble concentrating. Whenever she sat down to study, she got nervous. Her stomach tightened up, and her heart raced. Her grades were slipping, increasing her anxiety. She tried meditation, but found that when she sat still, her anxiety worsened. She believed in meditation. After all, her cognitive science professor had presented compelling evidence for meditation's calming effect on the nervous system. As she told us, "I'm here because my mind says yes, but my limbic and motor systems say no. Please help me!"

We began her therapy by working on a key principle of yoga: to link her mind and body. But for her we decided to approach it with a twist: do it in motion. She began with breathing meditations combined with simple body movements similar to the breathing meditations in this chapter. She practiced linking her attention to her movements in meditative breathing exercises and yoga postures. As she became aware in the present moment, she was shocked to realize how much her mind had jumped ahead. "I'm always thinking about what comes next—never what's happening now." She had been so caught up in graduate school and what lay ahead that she had lost her engagement with the present moment. She realized that by anticipating so much, she was actually avoiding facing her current concerns, doubts, and worries about her own self-worth. She used the yamas and niyamas to build inner strength. As she unified her attention with her actions in the here and now, she discovered a new sense of calm and confidence. Her anxiety subsided. Eventually, she was even able to sit still and meditate, but as a busy and ambitious young woman, she continued to prefer meditation in motion!

TYPES OF ANXIETY AND CHECKLISTS

People are troubled with anxiety in different ways. We have included a checklist for the many forms of anxiety, drawn from criteria used by therapists and doctors to help diagnose problems. But realize that labels can never fully explain what you are going through. You may find it helps to ease your anxiety if you better understand your tendencies and recognize what form of anxiety you are experiencing.

Check if you felt troubled with any of the items on the checklists for more than a few days over the past six months. If you find that you are severely and continually bothered by your anxiety, tell your therapist or seek a professional to work with you as you integrate yoga and mindfulness into your treatment.

Generalized Anxiety Disorder (GAD)

GAD involves a broad, overall feeling of anxiety that can inhibit you from doing things and going places. If you have GAD, you tend to approach your life with exaggerated and unrealistic worry and carry a great amount of tension, even though your worries are highly improbable.

FIGURE 12.1 GAD Checklist

	How often (daily, weekly)	Intensity (1 = least, 5 = greatest)	Circumstances when anxiety occurs	Circumstances when anxiety does not occur
Restless or on edge				
Tire easily				
Trouble concentrating				
Irritable				
Tight muscles				
Difficulty sleeping				

Social Anxiety Disorder (SAD)

SAD is felt in social situations and is experienced as intense worry, shyness, embarrassment, and self-consciousness. If you have SAD, you may feel as if others are judging you negatively or even ridiculing you. Sometimes the anxiety arises under specific circumstances, such as feeling uncomfortable speaking publicly. For others, it manifests as a generalized feeling of discomfort around people.

FIGURE 12.2 SAD Checklist

	How often (daily, weekly)	Intensity 1 = least, 5 = greatest	Circumstances when anxiety occurs	Circumstances when anxiety does not occur
Feel afraid, nervous, or uncomfortable in most social situations				
Feel anxious when meeting new people				
Get panicky when involved in certain kinds of social situations				
Avoid social situations				
Recognize that your feelings about social situations are extreme or unreasonable				

Panic Disorder

Panic disorder is often experienced as a severe physical crisis, such as a heart attack, when there is no real physical problem or danger. An intense panicky feeling strikes repeatedly without warning. If you have panic attacks, you might have uncomfortable physical symptoms such as pain in your chest, sweating, and irregular heartbeats.

FIGURE 12.3 Panic Disorder Checklists

	How often (daily, weekly)	Intensity (1 = least, 5 = greatest)	Circumstances when anxiety occurs	Circumstances when anxiety does not occur
Discomfort or pain in chest				
Chilled or hot (unrelated to menopause)				
Afraid of losing control				
Dizziness, light-headedness, or feeling faint				
Nausea or abdominal discomfort				
Heart pounding				
Shortness of breath				
Sense of pending doom				
Feeling of choking				
Sweating				
Trembling				
Feeling depersonalized or a sense of unreality				

Check if you have had any of these worries about panic attacks over the past month:

	How often (daily, weekly)	Intensity (1 = least, 5 = greatest)	Circumstances when anxiety occurs	Circumstances when anxiety does not occur
Continual worry about having a panic attack				
Concern about what might happen because of the attack				
Changing behavior because of a panic attack				
Fearing places or situations could be embarrassing or difficult to escape from without feeling panicky (agoraphobia)				

Specific Phobias

If you have a specific phobia, you have a fear of a particular thing, such as being afraid of dogs, heights, spiders, elevators, open spaces, or enclosed places. These fears are often initiated by a traumatic event. When you encounter the feared object, you probably experience an inordinate level of anxiety that is likely to cause you to avoid that feared object or situation.

FIGURE 12.4 Specific Phobia

	How often (daily, weekly)	Intensity (1 = least, 5 = greatest)	Circumstances when anxiety occurs	Circumstances when anxiety does not occur
Have a persistent and unreasonable fear of a specific object or situation				
Recognize your fear is excessive				
If faced with the object or situation, feeling intense discomfort				
The discomfort with this object or situation interferes with life in some way				

Obsessive-Compulsive Disorder (OCD)

OCD is also categorized as an anxiety problem. If you have OCD, you are likely to be plagued by disturbing thoughts (obsessions) and/or fears that make you feel compelled to perform particular actions or rituals (compulsions). For example, people diagnosed with OCD may have such a strong fear of infection that they feel compelled to wash their hands continually. Thoughts that plague people with OCD are often irrational and unrealistic.

FIGURE 12.5 OCD Checklist

	How often (daily, weekly)	Intensity (1 = least, 5 = greatest)	Circumstances when anxiety occurs	Circumstances when anxiety does not occur
Have intrusive and inappropriate and unrealistic obsessive thoughts, impulses, or images				
Try to suppress these thoughts, impulses, or images with another thought or action				
Recognize that these thoughts, impulses, or images are created by your own mind				
Perform a behavior or mental act aimed to stop the obsessive thoughts and decrease distress				
These behaviors are excessive and are not realistically connected to the thought impulse or image they are trying to prevent				
These behaviors take significant time out of your day and cause distress in themselves				

HOW ANXIETY AFFECTS YOUR NERVOUS SYSTEM

From the symptoms listed previously, you can clearly see that anxiety involves your mind *and* your body. In fact, your nervous system undergoes distinct changes when you are feeling anxious. Thus, it makes sense to work on both the mind and the body when treating anxiety.

Anxiety involves a number of brain systems that have a strong influence on what you feel and think. The thalamus acts as the doorway for signals received from the senses and passed along to other parts of the brain for processing. During an anxiety reaction, the amygdala, the gateway to the limbic system, alerts the hypothalamus that something is wrong. The hypothalamus, as the coordinator of internal functions, activates the fear/stress pathway (see Chapter 11, pages 84-85), which puts the autonomic nervous system on high alert. The hippocampus, where memories are processed, adds to the signal. In addition, the insula, which registers internal sensations, is activated by the inner discomforts. And, the cortex gets involved with disturbing thoughts and ruminations. The normal connectivity between the amygdala and frontal, occipital, and temporal lobes is decreased, leading to less successful regulation of emotions. With so many systems in the brain involved, you can understand why anxiety can be so pervasive and disruptive.

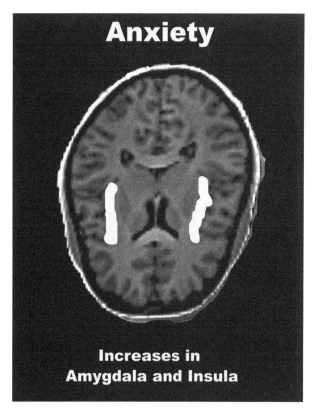

FIGURE 12.6 The Anxious Brain

Information Box: Neurotransmitter Imbalances Involved in Anxiety

1. Decreased activity of serotonin (5-HT). Serotonin inhibits the stress response
2. Gamma-aminobutyric acid (GABA), an inhibitory and calming neurotransmitter is lowered. Norepinephrine (noradrenaline), an excitatory neurotransmitter also involved in stress, is increased.
3. Corticotrophin-releasing hormone (CRH), a stress hormone, is increased, signaling the pituitary gland to release adrenocorticotrophic hormone, which in turn signals the adrenal gland to produce cortisol.

Typically, drug therapies used for anxiety increase the amount of GABA and serotonin, while decreasing norepenephrine and CRH in the system. The drugs help reduce over-excitation and elicit calming. But drugs are not the only way to alter the balance of neurotransmitters: Yoga and mindfulness can also be used to calm your system and rebalance your neurotransmitters.

ENGAGE YOUR WHOLE BEING FOR CHANGE: MIND, BODY, AND SPIRIT

Buddha told his followers that change is always two-sided: first, doing what is right and second, not doing what is wrong. It is very important when making a change that you stop doing unproductive, unhelpful things. You may have some simple lifestyle habits (sleep, diet, or exercise) that contribute to your discomfort. By making minor alterations in your daily routines, you create a basis for new possibilities to emerge. Then, as you become physically healthier, some of your anxiety will lessen.

Begin by observing your habits for eating, sleeping, and exercising using this chart. Keep in mind the mindfulness approach, and observe without judgment. Any change requires that you first observe what is really happening. Be objective as you note your weekly habits. This might help identify some fundamental ways that your habits are contributing to your anxiety.

FIGURE 12.7 Charting Your Habits

	Monday	Tuesday	Wednesday	Thursday	Friday	Saturday	Sunday
Hours of sleep							
Minutes of exercise							
What I ate for breakfast and when							
What I ate for lunch and when							
What I ate for dinner and when							
Hours of leisure							
Hours working							
Minutes of yoga and mindfulness practice							

Does your chart indicate that you are not sleeping enough, eating poorly, or rarely exercising? Perhaps anxiety is preventing you from changing your habits. Nonetheless, you can still make small changes—doing one or two things differently—to help you foster healthier habits. As the ancient Taoist sages taught, "The journey of 1000 miles begins with one step." Be open to the possibility of forging healthier habits, and you have already taken your first step.

Calming Your Anxiety

The nervous system changes when you are anxious: you may feel "hyped up," that is, highly aroused. This occurs from activation of the alertness center of the brain, the brain stem. You can diminish anxious feelings by deactivating this area. Begin the process by practicing calming regularly. Perform the calming exercises for stress in Chapter 11, pages 87-90, to initiate calming bottom-up. However, if you are like our client Teresa, sitting still may be hard for you to do. You might find it easier to practice active calming. You can begin a calming process more easily by breathing with motion, moving into yoga postures, and performing mindful walking.

Do the meditations for a short time at first, even just a few minutes, but do them several times during the day. If you have been chronically anxious for a long time, you will have stronger results by performing the exercises as often as possible. In time, your nervous system stabilizes in a calmer balance, and your anxiety reaction will ease. Start the process with these meditations to relax and release the breath while you move.

Release Your Breath: Chest Expansion Breathing

This exercise opens up your chest and allows the air to flow freely through your lungs. You gain greater calm and increased comfort from the opening of your chest, while also raising your energy level. Time your arm movements with your natural breathing.

Stand in mountain pose and extend your arms out directly in front of you as you exhale. Maintain your balance and let your arms swing around behind you, parallel to the floor while you inhale. Let the air fill your lungs fully as you allow your chest to expand. Exhale as you circle your hands back toward the front. Repeat this pattern several times, coordinating your breathing with the movement.

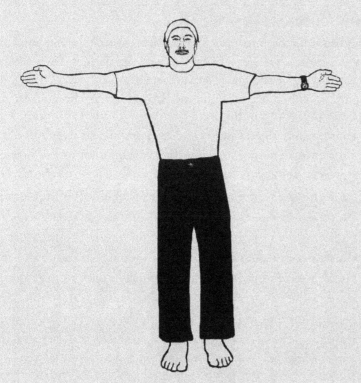 

FIGURE 12.8 Chest Expansion   **FIGURE 12.9** Chest Contraction

Free Your Breathing Passages: Cat's Breath

Have you ever watched a cat stretch, and marveled at its flexibility? The cat's breath is drawn from this elastic movement. Anxiety often correlates with rigidity in your breathing passages. Gently stretching and releasing these areas can restore flexibility to your breathing, like a cat. These two postures help you relax and stretch your back and midsection, coordinating your breathing with the movement.

Begin on your hands and knees. Inhale as you gently and slowly arch your back and raise your head to look straight in front of you. Feel the movement. Let the air fill your lungs completely. You should allow the releasing stretch along your entire back without pushing hard. Then exhale slowly and round your back carefully as you pull your stomach gently in and tuck your head down. Again, only do what is comfortable. Repeat the entire sequence several times, moving and breathing slowly with the movements. Keep the rest of your body relaxed, such as your jaw, face, and neck as well as your arms and legs. Maintain focused attention and move slowly.

FIGURE 12.10 Arched Back

FIGURE 12.11 Rounded Back

Postures for Anxiety Calming

Posture practice is an easy way to invite balance as you shift your attention away from intrusive thoughts and feelings. This simple series of postures is balanced and easy to perform. You can substitute other yoga routines. We suggest using poses that bring balance to both sides of your body by moving up and down, forward and backward, on one side and then the other. Rediscover your sense of balance through your body. Since the mind and body are linked, bringing balance to your body can lead to tranquility of your mind and centering in your life.

In general, when doing yoga postures, move into each position slowly and keep your mind focused on what you are doing as you do it. Pay attention to the subtle differences in tension and relaxation of various muscles. Observe your sensations and body posture. Keep your breathing in synchrony with the posture. Generally, inhale as you extend and exhale as you contract. Stay attuned at all times and you will derive deep benefit: from the simple comes the profound.

Relaxed Stretching Asana Series

Rest for a moment in the crocodile pose (see Figure 6.17). Lie prone on the floor with your head resting on your arms. Let your body relax completely. Gently breathe in and out, as you let go of any unnecessary tensions. Remain relaxed in this position until you are ready to continue the routine.

Now, as you are lying comfortably on your stomach, move your legs together and place the palms of your hands flat on the floor under your shoulders, elbows at your sides, and forehead resting on the floor to get ready for the cobra stretch (see Figure 11.8). Breathe in and out several times, relaxing in preparation. Inhale as you raise your chin and head up slowly. Let your gaze move upward as you bend your neck, carefully tensing, backward. Then lift your chest, curving your back up as you gradually raise your upper body, one vertebra at a time. Keep your hands on the floor, arms extended for support. Use your back muscles rather than pressing with your arm muscles to provide support while rising up in the cobra stretch. Keep your lower body relaxed, resting on the floor. When you get to the top, hold the position for 10 to 15 seconds as you breathe naturally. Then exhale as you reverse your motions, lowering yourself down very slowly, one vertebra at a time, relaxing your neck as you lower, and finally resting the back of your head on the floor.

Now, continue to lie on your stomach with your arms at your side and palms facing down on the floor. Push against the floor with your palms. Raise one of your legs up off the floor, as you inhale. Hold the position as you breathe in and out for a few seconds, and then slowly lower your leg. Next, perform the same motion with the other leg. Finally, if you have the strength, raise both legs together and hold as you breathe and relax everywhere else. Although you will need to tense some muscles, keep your upper body as relaxed as possible.

FIGURE 12.12 Half Locust Pose

Invite an Experience of Union, Well-being, and Peace: Samyama on Movement

Pick one of the movement exercises you liked best. Perform it now, allowing movement to occur naturally. Let your attention focus on the movement, and allow the motions to flow. Become completely absorbed in the movement without any conscious thought about it. Just be unified, mind, body, and spirit moving as one. As you permit this meditative union to develop, you will experience a sense of well-being and peace. Enjoy the moment!

ENLIST MINDFUL ATTENTION TO ALTER YOUR ANXIETY REACTION

When you are feeling anxious, you may often try *not* to feel it. But trying to avoid your anxiety can unwittingly make you feel more anxious. By becoming mindful, you can disentangle the web of your anxiety pattern. These exercises take you through a series of steps. Observe mindfully, without judging what you see. Trust that through this process, you will make some helpful discoveries that you can use in the next section. This series of exercises is especially helpful for people with GAD, panic attacks, OCD, and specific phobias.

Step 1: Become Mindfully Aware of Sensations, Thoughts, and Feelings

A pure sensation, thoughts about the sensation, and emotional reactions can be distinguished using mindfulness. This helps to loosen the strands in the web of your anxiety reaction. The first step is to notice the different components of your reaction: the various sensations, thoughts, and feelings.

Mindful Focus on Sensations

Start by turning your attention mindfully to the sensations of your anxiety. First attend to the qualities of breathing: sensory details, such as the air coming into your nose, its temperature, and the sound it makes in the passages. Each breath has its own group of sensations. Let your attention move to the feeling in your chest, stomach, or any other area that is associated with your breathing sensations. Notice how your rib cage lifts and drops with each breath, or how your stomach feels tight. Perhaps your face becomes warm.

Even if they are uncomfortable, simply observe and be curious about your sensory experience. Your sensations change, even though the change is subtle, with every passing moment. Allow your focus to move as your sensing unfolds.

Mindful of Thoughts

Anxiety usually engages a set of thoughts, likely in a repetitive pattern. Just as you learned how each breath is a combination of a number of sensations in the "Mindful Breathing" exercise (Chapter10, on page 77), so your anxiety reaction is a web of sensations interwoven with threads of repetitive thoughts, probably negative interpretations, and worries, along with characteristic moods and emotions.

> *Pay attention to your thinking process. Do your best not to get caught up in any particular thought. Instead, take a step back as if you are watching the whole pattern move in the wind. The shapes and patterns shift, sometimes more thoughts occur, sometimes less. Observe your patterns of thought as they change over time.*

Mindful of Feelings

> *Now pay attention to any emotions concerning anxiety that may be occurring along with those thoughts. Simply notice what emotions you feel as you feel them. Don't assess these emotions or think more about them. Once again, just observe.*

Mindful of the Interconnections

> *Take a step back and pay attention to the connection between one thing and another, such as how a thought might be tied to a sensation or a feeling. Do you notice a characteristic order? Perhaps you have a thought or sensation followed by a feeling. Or maybe it goes the other way. Simply notice the flow, moment by moment as you become familiar with the patterns you observe.*

Step 2: Mindful Before, During, and After

You probably have situations, people, thoughts, or memories that tend to trigger an anxiety reaction. Practice your mindfulness meditation in different situations when anxiety arises.

> *Are you aware of the moment right before your anxiety occurs? Pay attention to what triggered the reaction. Notice whether the anxiety comes on quickly or builds gradually over time. Observe that building process: Are you telling yourself frightening, awful, or worrisome things?*
>
> *Now, listen to your inner talk while you are having an anxiety reaction, but do so mindfully. Observe whether the conversation comes in a cascade of thoughts about what is going on within, or in trickles of words, individual ideas. Notice any emotions that are evoked by the thoughts. Observe associated sensations, and how they develop over time. Pay attention to each experience as it occurs.*
>
> *Finally, observe mindfully as your anxiety eases. Did you do anything to bring that about, or did it just happen? When anxiety recedes, does it do so suddenly, or do you feel it easing a little bit at a time? Take note of the sensations, thoughts, and feelings associated with the end of your anxiety reaction. Paradoxically, sometimes it is easier to recognize that you were anxious immediately following an anxiety reaction. Perhaps the contrast helps recognition. Mindfulness makes recognition more evident.*
>
> *At the end of this chapter, you will find guidelines for journaling and charting. Take a few moments to record what you have learned about your triggers, how you sustain your anxiety, and how to help it diminish and even leave entirely.*

Step 3: Meditative Unlearning and Relearning

Years of anxiety condition groups of neurons to form links in the brain. Meditation practice can literally rewire your nervous system by interrupting the anxiety reaction and substituting calm instead. The change occurs all the way down at the neuronal connections. The practice draws on your ability to relax, which you have been practicing all through this workbook, and your ability to focus your attention, which you have also trained by working through the exercises in this workbook. Meditative re-learning is most helpful for anxiety that is targeted to something you can identify, such as specific fears and social anxiety. But you can vary it to fit your situation. The example we use here is fear of water. Substitute your own fear, anxiety, or trigger with appropriate variations. Work gradually, building your skills, step by step. Repeat this meditation regularly until you are able to stay calm all the way through.

Allow your muscles to relax. Warm up with a visualization exercise. Perhaps you could picture a pleasant place where you felt very comfortable. Relax and enjoy the image. Once you have reached a deep feeling of comfort, begin by thinking very generally about your fear. If it is a fear of water, contemplate water in general, thinking about water in a distant way. Picture yourself far away from a body of water, such as the ocean, a lake, or a pool, perhaps behind a high fence. Maintain deep relaxation and begin to imaginatively walk toward the water. If you start to feel tense, pause in your imagery, backtrack, and reestablish your deep relaxation. Continue to relax deeply, as you imagine being barely able to see the water at a distance. The first day, you may want to stop quite a distance away.

At a second session, try again. Begin with relaxed breathing or an image of a beautiful place you enjoy. Then, picture yourself gradually moving closer and closer to the water, but always backtrack if you feel fear or discomfort. Take as long as you need. Keep working with this image until you can enter the water and remain calm. Then, let yourself gradually step deeper, maintaining your calm breathing, in and out. Continue to breathe comfortably until you have successfully entered the water while remaining relaxed. Maintaining a meditative calm generates a ripple of healing.

Repeat this exercise over several days or even weeks. Check out your reactions by thinking about water when you are not meditating and notice what you feel. You may surprise yourself. A carefully constructed hierarchy, from the least threatening to the most threatening may help you gradually face your situation with confidence and master it.

Step 4: Acceptance

How can you integrate all your new learning into your life? Begin with acceptance. Mindfulness is a process of accepting each experience, each sensation, thought, or feeling, just as it is. Its practice reveals a depth and breadth of experience that is usually missed or ignored. As you observe the fabric of your experiencing more closely, you probably can see some things you like and some things you don't. You might ask yourself why would I want to accept an uncomfortable feeling or unpleasant sensation? Paradoxically, by accepting everything, the good as well as the bad, you transform. Through the practice of accepting and letting be, you will discover your potential to be at peace with who you are.

So first, find a time when you are feeling comfortable to perform your mindfulness meditation. Next, practice at times when you are feeling anxious. In both situations, accept each moment's experience as just that—an experience. Practice this way for one minute, then two and three—extending to as long as you can. If your attention wanders or you find yourself worrying or telling yourself how awful it is, stop, take a relaxed breath, and go back to being aware. Don't chastise yourself, just take note of it, and return to the meditation. By treating yourself gently and kindly—literally accepting whatever you experience as okay—you open the way to being more comfortable with yourself.

JOURNALING AND CHARTING

Keeping a journal and charting can be helpful as you become aware of the entire process of eliciting, producing, maintaining, and letting go of an anxiety reaction. Once you become aware of your triggers, cycles, and patterns, you can alter the automatic response and lessen the discomfort. Be aware of your responses and write them down. Remember to reflect on them mindfully, and later, update your journal with new discoveries and observations.

Issues Revealed by Mindfulness in Your Journal

When you practice mindfulness of things that bother you, conflicts lose their hold and dissolve. Research has supported that mindfulness is effective alone, without directly addressing personal issues. But sometimes, unresolved issues may still emerge, needing to be attended to, worked through, and let go of when appropriate. You can work some of these issues through by journaling. If the issues are too painful or difficult to face alone, or you realize you are feeling defensive, bring this material to your therapist. The following questions will help guide your mindfulness meditation as you work toward resolution:

- What situations or activities do I find most comfortable?
- What situations tend to trigger anxiety?
- How do I feel just before I encounter a trigger?
- How do I perpetuate an anxiety reaction or even make it worse? What are the typical things I tell myself when I feel anxious? Am I adding a threatening quality?

- Could I interpret my situation differently, such that I would not find the situation anxiety provoking?
- How can I help myself to feel more comfortable when I am having an anxiety reaction? What situations or activities help me to feel more comfortable when I am having an anxiety reaction? List the possibilities.
- What situations can I use or activities can I do to prevent me from having an anxiety reaction?

CHARTING TIMES WITHOUT ANXIETY

You have explored when you are anxious, but it is equally valuable to turn your awareness to those times when you are not anxious. Keep a chart to observe when you are not having anxiety. As you become more aware of the moments when you are comfortable and at ease, you will be better able to extend and deepen them.

FIGURE 12.13 Without Anxiety Chart

	Monday	Tuesday	Wednesday	Thursday	Friday	Saturday	Sunday
What you felt right before feeling anxious							
Triggers for anxiety							
Triggers for calm feelings							
Note times you are not feeling anxious and how long it lasts							
Describe comfortable experiences: sensations, thoughts, emotions that arise							

CHAPTER 13

Overcoming Trauma and Regaining Confidence

*The future has yet to be made. Our present choices give a new form
even to the past so that what it means depends on what we do now.*

—Radhakrishnan, former president of
India and yoga scholar, 1977

IN THIS CHAPTER

- Distinguish traumatic stress disorders from posttraumatic growth
- Describe the neuroscience of traumatic stress
- Use meditation to self-regulate and calm your nervous system
- Practice yoga postures to build resilience and regain self-confidence
- Create an experience of safety and security wherever you are
- Mindfully observe trauma triggers, emotions, thoughts, and behaviors
- Reconsolidate traumatic memories for lasting change
- Alter trauma patterns

INTRODUCTION

If you have experienced trauma, you have had an experience involving threat of death or serious injury to yourself or someone else. Statistics show that although trauma can have harmful effects, it may also stimulate resilience and toughness, and result in meaningful change. In fact, researchers have found that moderate amounts of adversity can be good for you, enabling you to handle future stressors better (Meichenbaum, 2012). Traumatic stress offers an opportunity to reach a higher level of functioning.

Of course, taking an optimistic view of trauma doesn't trivialize the horrors you might have endured. Your nervous system went through a shock, and what you experienced was extremely disturbing. Long after traumatic events, your nervous system may remain off balance. And you will likely continue to have disturbing memories and worries that may interfere with your everyday life; however, if you have been working your way through this workbook, you know by now that your nervous system has a great deal of plasticity. In fact, it can be quite resilient. And so, you *can* intervene! With yoga and mindfulness practices, you can transform your trauma into an opportunity to grow.

Yoga and mindfulness provide you with a clear path to calm your nervous system, cultivate your inner strength, and find inspiration in higher values. By engaging your mind, brain, and body, you will hone your resilience. You will be equipped to rise above your initial negative experience, cope successfully with difficulties that must be endured, and overcome problems that can be changed. The meditations and exercises in this section along with the exercises in the other chapters in Part III help you reclaim your life and forge a healthier, happier you!

The Girl Who Turned Her Trauma Around

Jessica had a warm, sheltered upbringing in a small town in a nearby state. She had a bubbly personality and was sometimes accused of being a "ditz" as she told us, but she didn't care because she was just having too much fun at college. One day she was walking back to her college campus dorm room along the path from the local town. Her mind was miles away. She had taken a short break from exam week studying to do a little shopping. Her backpack was filled with the fortifying snacks she bought for her friends in the dorm. Her attention was brought back to her walk when she heard a rustling in the woods up ahead. She thought, "Oh, that's nothing" and kept walking. Then she saw a dark, shadowy figure far up ahead, but dismissed its significance as she continued on her way. Suddenly, a disheveled, heavyset man jumped out from the woods, right in front of her. She had a fearful thought about it, but then dismissed her concern with a trusting thought, "Oh, these things don't happen here." Suddenly he was right next to her, reaching out to grab her arm. She froze, thinking, "This can't be happening to me!" As he threw her roughly to the ground, she tried to scream, but it was too late.

Jessica quit school and moved back home, unable to do anything. She saw danger lurking all around her and was afraid to even leave the house. She felt depressed and angry, and often took her anger out on herself. She couldn't stop remembering the horror of the experience and blamed herself for being an unsuspecting fool in such a scary world. Her trust had become mistrust; her confidence had been replaced by fear and anger.

Yoga and mindfulness were key elements in Jessica's therapy. She practiced a yoga strength routine given in this chapter several times a week to build up physically. She learned mindfulness, bringing her attention to the present moment, to deepen her awareness and put her in touch with the safety of her parents' home where she was currently living. Gradually she regained trust in others and in herself. She became more grounded in what she was doing in the present, actual world. She gradually developed confidence that she would recognize and face a threat if it ever happened again, without expecting threat from every dark shadow. Because of this work, her memories were altered. She reconsolidated her shattering traumatic experience into a new, more confident perspective: Though she had lost her innocence, she reclaimed it, through transforming the meaning of her trauma. She used her experience by volunteering as a counselor to help others who had been through trauma. She told us, "I feel somehow vindicated when I realize that my experience, awful though it was, allowed me to be able to help someone else." Eventually, she returned to college and earned a degree in psychology. When we talked to her some months later, she had started a job working professionally at a trauma center, where she could apply what she learned to help others.

Information Box: Neuroscience of Trauma

We have an unconscious system that helps us to detect a threat to our safety, a brain-body response at the level of the nervous system known as neuroception (Porges, 2011). Several brain systems with a link to cognition and emotions are involved. When facing a perceived threat, your amygdala sends messages to your endocrine system as part of the stress pathway that links the hypothalamus, pituitary, and adrenal glands together. Please review Chapter 11, pages 84-85, where we described the details of the fear/stress pathway. Thus, this pathway is not only activated by an immediate threat but is also triggered by memories of the traumatic event. This arises because the hippocampus, where memories are stored, is closely linked to the amygdala. The proximity and interaction of these brain areas helps to explain how you keep remembering the threat even though it occurred in the past.

TRAUMA CATEGORIES

There are three main categories of trauma disorders, each with known causes and characteristic reactions. The disorder checklists can help you to categorize the kind of trauma you have experienced. A growth chart is also provided to help you reroute your experience into something transformative.

Acute Stress Disorder (ASD)

If you had a single traumatic event, such as one resulting from a car accident or a damaging storm, but have otherwise led a normal life, you have what is called an ASD. ASD sufferers tend to get over the trauma in several months, especially with meditation and brief psychotherapy.

Posttraumatic Stress Disorder (PTSD)

PTSD has become one of the most pervasive problems in modern times. When trauma recurs, such as from a war, rape, or a serious one-time trauma, the diagnosis will be PTSD. Recovery often takes longer than ASD. The most extreme form of PTSD derives from horrific events, such as when active-duty soldiers face death and mutilations, women endure multiple rapes, or children grow up in war-torn areas. These kinds of severe trauma usually require long-term treatment.

Developmental Trauma Disorder (DTD)

DTD occurs if you have been raised with continual abuse, lacked a supportive environment or grown up in a war-torn area. If you have a diagnosis of DTD, you should find a good therapist who can provide you with support over time. We recommend someone who is sympathetic to yoga and mindfulness or hypnosis, since these methods have been shown to be especially helpful for traumatic stress problems. Part of helpful therapy involves guidance in how to develop healthy psychological and physical habits, which you may not have acquired as a child.

FIGURE 13.1 ASD, PTSD, and DTD Checklist

	How often (daily, weekly)	Intensity (1 = least, 5 = greatest)	Circumstances when anxiety occurs	Circumstances when anxiety does not occur
Experienced or witnessed a life-threatening or dangerous frightening event and felt fear, horror, or helplessness				
Continue to re-experience the traumatic event as disturbing memories, dreams, emotions, and/or physical symptoms				
Try to avoid anything that is associated with the trauma				
Feel a generalized numbing				
Have difficulty sleeping				
Feel irritable and have angry outbursts				
Overly vigilant				
Startle easily				
Have problems concentrating				

Posttraumatic Growth (PTG)

PTG is the change people undergo from the struggles they endure when meeting an extremely challenging situation. Surprisingly, some people who endure a trauma eventually become more flexible, stronger, and more resilient. Following the challenges of trauma, you can be transformed and strengthened. The growth does not occur from the trauma, but from how you deal with it.

Even if you have not experienced all of the indicators of PTG, we encourage you to fill out this checklist again after you have worked through the chapter. Give yourself some time, and you will find more to check off!

FIGURE 13.2 Posttraumatic Growth Checklist

Fill out this checklist now, and then fill it out again after you have read this chapter (see Figure 13.10).

	How often (daily, weekly)	Intensity (1 = least 5 = greatest)	Circumstances when anxiety occurs	Circumstances when anxiety does not occur
Have a greater appreciation for life				
Changed your priorities				
Gained a greater sense of personal strength				
Have a deeper sense of spirituality				
Have been able to grieve				
Can accept the trauma				
Have supportive people around you				
Found new meaning for your life				
Want to move forward				
Wish you could help others				

BUILDING RESILIENCE

You have inherent inner strength. If you are a soldier, you have probably had experiences of being strong and capable. And even those not in the military probably did not feel helpless, fearful, or lacking in confidence before the traumatic event. Yoga poses can build your feeling of strength and confidence bottom up, as you take a strong body posture. The key point of the therapeutic application of these postures is to feel strength and extend it confidently. Pushing your body posture is not the goal. Instead, be comfortable as you use these postures to build and express your power!

Embody Strength: Warrior Postures

The warrior sequence is symbolic of taking a strong stand, and you will feel your natural capacity to be a strong person as you embody the warrior series. Move slowly in and out of each position, keeping your motions smooth. Hold each position as long as you can, breathing in and out, and then move slowly into the next position.

FIGURE 6.18 Warrior 1

Perform the first warrior pose in this sequence as described in Chapter 6, in the exercise "Taking a Confident Stance in the Warrior Pose" on page 54.

FIGURE 13.3 Warrior 2

Face your chest and torso toward the right so that your whole body faces squarely right. You may let your back foot pivot diagonally to take the strain off your knees. Raise your arms straight over your head with palms facing forward and arch your back gently with the inhale. Hold for several seconds as you breathe comfortably in and out several times. Then lower your arms back to the first warrior position as you exhale.

FIGURE 13.4 Warrior 3

Exhale as you lean to the right, resting the elbow of your right arm on your right knee. Extend your left hand overhead and toward the right as you lean your upper body to the right. Feel a stretch through your right arm, waist, and left leg. Repeat all three positions on the other side. Perform the entire sequence twice.

Strength Building with the T-Pose

Your feeling of self-support comes from your legs. The expression "To stand on your own two feet" means to be self-sufficient and capable of handling your life. When you are physically stronger, you will find it easier to stand up to the challenges you face. The T-pose will strengthen your legs and back, while toning your abdominal areas. It also strengthens your knees. And as a balance asana, it will enhance your concentration. All of these qualities will increase your resilience and confidence.

Begin doing this exercise with the support of a counter or wall. Stand upright, about three feet away from your support. Raise your arms up overhead and inhale. Bring one leg up behind you as you lower your upper body parallel with the floor. Let your extended hands rest on the support. Your body will be in the shape of a T. Look at one spot on the floor as you keep your neck straight. Sense where your balance point is. If you feel steady enough, lift your hands slightly away from the support, to balance on your own. Breathe in and out as you hold this position as long as you can comfortably.

FIGURE 13.5 T-Pose 1

Next, bend your supporting knee as you maintain the position with your hands extended in front. Don't perform the knee-bending part of this exercise if you have knee problems. But if your knees feel comfortable, keep your arms parallel to the floor and hold with your leading knee bent, and then straighten again. When you feel ready, return to the mountain pose (standing upright). Continue to stand in the mountain pose for a moment or two, then rest. Once you feel adequately rested, repeat on the other side.

FIGURE 13.6 T-Pose 2

Fierce Like a Lion

Adding strength is not just a matter of discipline or building muscle. It also requires a strengthening of the spirit. Yoga draws from the spirit of animals to bring out the practitioner's inner strength. Each animal has a different spirit to draw from. For example, stretching like a cat adds flexibility and resiliency. The cobra's coiling ability can be translated into making your spine stronger and more flexible. And you can draw from a lion's ferocity to raise your vitality and develop the stronger side of your nature. Perform the lion pose with power and intensity. This pose helps to tone your facial muscles and releases emotional tension. Following the exercise your face and neck areas will feel more relaxed.

The lion is performed in the pelvic pose, in a kneeling position. If sitting on the floor is uncomfortable, you can do this posture from a chair. Place your hands on your knees and inhale completely. Then exhale sharply as you learn forward. At the same time, tense and separate your fingers, tense the muscles in your face and neck, open your eyes and mouth wide, and stick out your tongue. Hold for approximately 15 seconds and then slowly withdraw your tongue; relax your eyes, face, and neck; relax your fingers; and settle back into the pelvic posture. Repeat several times. Between sets, relax your muscles and breathe gently.

FIGURE 13.7 Lion

NURTURING YOUR SENSE OF SAFETY

You can create your own sense of safety using yoga postures and meditation. These practices develop a calm center that can bring out a sense of being secure from within. Without dependence on anything outside of your own resources, you may find refuge in the following meditative moment.

Self-Soothing with a Posture

Certain yoga postures can enhance your ability to regulate your own emotions, by calming your nervous system and quieting your mind. The child pose is a posture for self-soothing with a special comforting quality. It provides a feeling of self-support that can be reassuring especially when you are feeling unsafe and insecure. Here are several variations.

Sit on your feet in the kneeling pelvic pose (see Figure 6.15). Bend forward slowly until your cheek touches the floor. Allow your arms to rest comfortably at your sides with your elbows bent so that they can relax on the floor (see Figure 6.19 Child Pose). For a variation, rest your forehead on the floor as you extend your arms out in front of your head, for another experience of self-support, as your arms cradle around your head. You may need to shift or move slightly to find the most comfortable position. Breathe calmly and rest in this position. If you have trouble sitting on the floor, try the child pose while sitting on a chair at a table. Lay your head facedown on the table. Place your arms next to your head on either side. Breathe comfortably for several minutes. You will feel protected and supported in all of these soothing child poses.

FIGURE 13.8 Child Pose 2

Visualizing Sanctuary

Meditation can help create a sense of comfort and security. Practice this visualization regularly to initiate a change in your sense of safety.

Think of a time when you felt calm and comfortable. Usually people think of a tranquil place in nature, but you might also have a memory of being in a room that you enjoyed or with loved ones. Recall that place, and how you felt when you were there or imagine how you would feel if you went there. What do you see and hear? Sense the aromas in the air, the feeling of a breeze and sun on your skin. Vividly picture yourself there. Draw on your own experiences from the past or even a fictional place from a book or movie. Visualize a sanctuary and go there to rest.

A Clear Mind: Your Own Inner Sanctuary

Sanctuary is always possible in the here and now moment of mindful presence. You can carry peace of mind with you always and anywhere.

Sit quietly in meditation. Let all your sensations settle. Breathe comfortably, in and out, allowing your breathing rate to be relaxed and calm. Now clear your mind of all thoughts. As soon as a new thought appears, let it go and meditate in the present moment. Keep working on letting your stream of consciousness be clear of any thought outside of this quiet moment. Now, sitting quietly, there is no worry, fear, or stress. Everything is serene and peaceful. Here is true sanctuary, always available if you simply make the effort to recognize that it is there.

Opening Your Root Chakra to Nurture Feelings of Security and Safety

The root chakra (see Figure 5.4) is located at the base of the spine, where your body rests when you are sitting cross-legged on the floor or on a chair. This chakra represents security and support. Focusing on this area will nurture feelings of safety from your own internal core.

> *Sit comfortably on the ground outside, cross-legged in the easy pose. (If sitting on the ground is uncomfortable, perform this meditation sitting in a comfortable chair.) Close your eyes and focus your attention on the root chakra, at the base of your spine. Visualize the color red, spreading out from your base, bringing strength and stability with each breath in and out. Feel your connection to the ground where you sit (or feel the support from the chair). Draw from its strength and stability. Visualize each breath in, flowing down to your root, connecting you to the stability of the ground, and then flowing out again as you exhale, relaxed and calm. Enjoy this moment, grounded in the present, stable, strong, and capable, arising now from your own root.*

Altering Your Trauma Patterns

> *Trauma is stored in your memory. In general, memory has two main systems:*
>
> 1. *Explicit memory is conscious and engages in recalling your daily experiences, known as episodic memory. It works through your prefrontal cortex—the thinking brain and the hippocampus—where memories are stored.*
> 2. *Implicit memory is unconscious and emotional. These memories are amygdala centered and are not immediately accessible to conscious awareness.*

Traumatic memories are often stored as implicit memories. They are not easy to change. When you experience a trauma, the overwhelming intensity of experiencing triggers a rush of neurotransmitters that activate the HPA pathway. This blocks your explicit memory system, leading to amnesia of the event itself, preventing you from remembering exactly what happened; however, since the traumatic event is processed through the emotional limbic system as well, it is stored as an unconscious, implicit memory. So a simple cue, even remotely related, could elicit a flood of patterned reactions, entrenching the traumatic memory in your brain.

You can initiate a change in your typical trauma pattern and literally rewire your brain so that the reaction will no longer be the same. The next series of exercises takes you through a process of (1) becoming mindfully aware of the pattern and (2) changing the pattern in several ways so that you reconsolidate the memory in a new, less disturbing way.

Mindful Awareness

Your trauma pattern has four key elements:

1. Triggers
2. Emotional responses
3. Corresponding thoughts
4. Typical behaviors

Begin by mindfully observing each of these elements, and you will shift your traumatic memory from being implicit and unconscious, leading to a reaction that is out of control, to becoming explicit, conscious, and manageable, putting you in the driver's seat of your reaction and back in control.

Mindful of Triggers

We have seen with our clients who have been through trauma that some learn to know exactly what triggers a reaction, and others don't. For example, soldiers often learn that any loud noise will elicit their reaction, but a woman who was molested as a child may not be able to pinpoint her triggers.

> *Practice mindfulness in the moment when your reaction is triggered. Stop and pay attention to what you are experiencing as it happens. At first, you may not think to practice until after your reaction has already been triggered, but whenever you start, this process will prove helpful. In time you will become aware more quickly, so don't be discouraged. Remember to suspend judgment, observe, and trust that mindful awareness will be helpful.*

Mindful of Emotions

As soon as you react, notice your emotions. What do you feel? Observe your sensations (such as your heart beating, palms sweating, or stomach tightening) and your feelings (for example, panic, frightened, or angry) and any other experiences you might be having. Try to assess the intensity of your reactions, and whether your experience alters as time passes. Once again, even if they are somewhat uncomfortable, stay calm, at a manageable distance, with the qualities of the experience as best you can. With your mindful eye, you can watch the dark clouds of your experiences flow past, with their distinct patterns changing moment by moment. In so doing, this will help you to feel a little less threatened, as you see clear skies on the horizon. Trust the process because you are developing helpful abilities that will alter the effects of your traumatic experience.

Mindful of Thoughts

Now observe the thought patterns that arise. Notice just what you are saying to yourself when you have the emotional reaction. You may be telling yourself negative, scary things. If you perceive negativity, watch how your thinking unfolds. Do your thoughts become increasingly negative? Do you get into an internal argument? Do your thoughts repeat or are you thinking a long, escalating series of thoughts? If you find yourself carried away by a particular stream of thought at some point, climb back on shore as soon as you can and resume observing objectively.

Mindful of Behaviors

Now turn your attention to your behavior. What do you typically do when you start feeling and thinking that way? Do you withdraw and keep to yourself? Or perhaps you explode with anger? Or maybe you find yourself crying? How does your body respond? Perhaps it tightens up, or just feels fatigued? As always, observe your typical behaviors nonjudgmentally.

Easing Your Reaction by Contrast

At a time when you are not feeling disturbed, take a few mindful moments to sit quietly in the comfort of your home, out in nature, or even in the therapy office. Allow your breathing to be comfortable and let yourself relax. Mindfully observe the sensations, thoughts, and feelings you have as you are safely sitting there. Enjoy the security and comfort for several minutes.

Now, allow yourself to think briefly about the traumatic pattern that you worked with in the previous four exercises. Remind yourself that you are in a different place physically and mentally. You are re-examining the memory now in the safety of your own home or therapist's office.

Remain as calm as you can in the present moment, and notice the details, but with a difference. Breathe and deliberately relax as you let yourself ponder the reality that nothing dangerous was really happening when your reaction was last triggered.

If your emotions begin to rise, counter them with a reassurance that you are okay as you sit centered in this quiet moment. You might find your feelings escalate, and if so, look around you and pay attention to where you are now, to allow yourself to become comfortable again.

When you are calm once more, observe your thought patterns during this reaction. Perhaps you are telling yourself how awful it was, how unfair it was, how disturbed you were, or some other "uh-oh" type of thought. Notice how these thoughts fuel your emotions. Try to recall that, no matter how terrible it was, you survived. The horrible time has passed.

Nurturing Self-Support and Self-Acceptance

The experience you have while meditating brings a sense of how you are the master of your life. You may not be able to control contingency, but you can control how you interpret it. You can be ever more at peace, even when you have experienced a traumatic event, by cultivating acceptance meditatively.

Meditate on breathing for a few minutes, noticing each breath, in and out. Your breathing finds its own natural rhythm. All you have to do is allow it to happen. Many things are like this. When you have the flu, you can drink extra water and get sufficient rest, but ultimately, nature takes its course and your body eventually heals. This is also true of trauma. If you take care of your physical and psychological health, your brain-mind-body system will find its natural balance again. Nature will take its course. Can you think of other examples of how the mind-brain-body system restores balance of itself? As you sit in meditation, accept that this natural healing process can help you now. Trust that you can return to normal when the time is right, allowing your recovery process to take the time it needs. Our brains are capable of growing and developing as needed. Have confidence in the process.

Adopt a mindful nonjudgmental attitude whenever you find yourself revving up your reactions by telling yourself how bad it was and how terrible you feel. Keep working on letting these evaluations go. Although the event might have been terrible, your negative judgments will not reduce the effects. Instead, bring yourself into the present moment and focus on your present experience. Keep working on questioning any negative evaluations. When you can accept what is, you open the way to changing your trauma pattern so that it will no longer trouble you.

SUSTAINING PRACTICE WITH CHARTING AND JOURNALING

You have initiated a healing process. By regularly calming your emotions, letting go of negative thinking, and accepting yourself, you will begin to feel more at ease in the world.

Changing a long-standing pattern takes repeated practice. You are reversing what may have become an entrenched pattern, and it may take time to shift the balance and feel the effects. Journaling and charting can help you sustain the process.

Journaling

Witnessing evil or death transforms you. By touching the depths, you reach the heights. You can now steer your life by following an enlightened compass and remaining attuned to what is truly important and meaningful for you.

Read through the yamas and niyamas again, and reflect on each one, finding inspiration to help you guide your life in a better direction.

1. Can you seek higher values?
2. Would you like to take a new direction for work or relationships?
3. Are you interested in helping others?
4. Having suffered, do you have greater compassion for other people's suffering?
5. List the ways you would like to fulfill your potential.

CHARTING

FIGURE 13.9 Charting Your Practice

	Yama and niyama reflections	Posture practice	Mindfulness and meditation practice
Monday morning midday evening			
Tuesday morning midday evening			

(Continued)

FIGURE 13.9 *(Continued)*

Wednesday morning midday evening			
Thursday morning midday evening			
Friday morning midday evening			
Saturday morning midday evening			
Sunday morning midday evening			

CHARTING YOUR POSTTRAUMATIC GROWTH OVER TIME

Fill out this chart again after you have gone through the chapter. Continue to return to it from time to time to observe tangible changes you are making. You may have other qualities to add to this list. Please feel free to make your own creative discoveries!

FIGURE 13.10 Posttraumatic Growth Checklist 2

	How often (daily, weekly)	Intensity (1 = least, 5 = most)	Circumstances when anxiety occurs	Circumstances when anxiety does not occur
Have a greater appreciation for life				
Changed your priorities				
Gained a sense of personal strength				
Have a deeper sense of spirituality				
Have been able to grieve				
Can accept the trauma				
Have supportive people around you				
Found new meaning for your life				
Want to move forward				
Wish you could help others				
Other positive changes you have observed				

CHAPTER 14

Alleviating Depression and Fostering Well-being

The perfect way knows no difficulties
Except that it refuses to make preferences;
If you wish to see it before your own eyes
Have no fixed thoughts either for or against it.
—Paraphrased from Seng-Ts'an,
Hsin-Hsin Ming, first Zen poem

IN THIS CHAPTER

- Effect of depression on the brain
- Activating your nervous system with breathing and postures
- Altering negative thinking with mindfulness
- Regulating emotions for better self-control
- Fostering well-being with gratitude and compassion

INTRODUCTION

Depression brings distinct nervous system changes fueled by an over-activated frontal cortex, low arousal of the nervous system, and poor affect regulation. Mindfulness techniques can interrupt the consequent negative ruminating by intervening in the process of self-critical thinking itself. In addition, yoga postures and breathing combined with meditation can restore normal arousal levels. The regular practice of yoga and mindfulness, with the feelings of well-being it brings, can help you find greater enjoyment in everyday life.

The Man Who Took Hold of His Depression and Changed It

Matt was a promising innovator in his field. He had gotten a high-paying job immediately after graduating with his master's degree. He seemed to be bound for success. But his progress got snarled only a year later by lawsuits and patent disputes over his inventions. Feeling blocked, discouraged, and unable to produce, he quit his job and slid into a dark depression. Now in his early 40s, he was bitter. Deep lines were carved into his face. By the time he finally sought therapy, he had been spending long hours alone in his house, ruminating about his negative experiences. He felt helplessly out of control.

With mindfulness meditation, he learned to distinguish between his experiences and his judgments about his experiences. He was surprised to notice how much of his thinking was negative. We encouraged him to keep noticing what he was experiencing in the present without evaluating it. He soon noticed how one negative thought led to the next and how the progression increased his disturbance. He also perceived positive things he had been ignoring, such as how the grass moved in the wind, and the caring support he was receiving from his family. With practice, he eventually became more able to stay in the present moment, leaving his negativity behind. He soon had periods without feeling depressed.

As he distanced himself further from his negative thoughts, he began to feel his motivation return. He took a part-time job with a small company. We encouraged him to remain mindful as he worked. He encountered some minor tensions and began to feel bombarded by old worry patterns again. But with our encouragement he maintained his mindful attention without judging. Much to his surprise, he was able to distinguish between his new situation and the old one after we drew his attention to relevant details. These observations allowed him to remain open, realistic, and flexible. His newfound objectivity helped keep him mindful of his task, and he did his job well. His company succeeded with the project he was working on, which further enhanced his feeling of confidence. Looking back he observed, "Meditation helps me distinguish a real problem from an imagined one. I am able to keep my ego out of situations and do my best, regardless. Mindfulness really is a great tool!"

How Depression Changes Your Brain

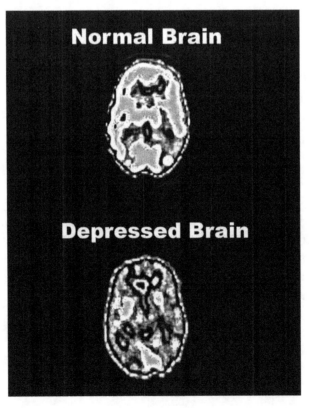

FIGURE 14.1 A Depressed Brain Compared with a
Normal Brain

Information: How Depression Alters the Brain

1. Rumination over-activates parts of the prefrontal cortex.
2. Your nervous system is under-activated, correlating with difficulties doing things and thinking well.
3. Decreased connectivity between the limbic (emotional) system and the frontal (thinking) areas results in poor decisions and inability to regulate negative emotions. Rational planning and intention to change become ineffective.
4. Meditation regulates affect by increasing the connectivity between limbic and frontal areas. Change becomes possible.
5. Yoga breathing and postures gently activate the nervous system.
6. Mindful nonjudgmental awareness deactivates frontal areas, thus diminishing ruminations.

ACTIVATE YOUR NERVOUS SYSTEM

When you are depressed, and your nervous system is under-activated, your mood drops to a lower level. Yoga and mindfulness encourage your energy to flow freely, providing gentle methods of stimulation. The result is a gentle, pleasant lifting of your depressed mood.

Breathing Exercises for Vitalizing

Lie down in savasana (see Figure 6.16). *Raise your knees and place your feet flat on the floor so that your back rests flat on the floor. As you inhale through your nose, raise your rib cage and arch your back slightly as you allow the air to move down into your lungs. As you exhale gently, press your back slightly in the opposite direction against the floor. Repeat the gentle movements coordinated with your breathing for several minutes. Remember not to force the movements or the breathing. Stay relaxed. This pranayama will vitalize you while relaxing physical tensions.*

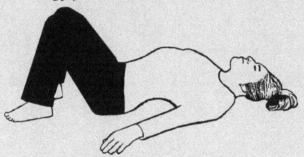

FIGURE 14.2 Savasana Breathing

The Complete Breath

One of the best exercises for vitalizing is the regular practice of the complete breath. Start with some complete breaths in a standing position. When you perform the complete breath, remember to remain relaxed throughout. Breathe in through your nose and let the air move all the way down, expanding your abdomen, then contract and let it out again. Detailed instructions for the complete breath are found in the section "The Complete Breath" in Chapter 5, page 40.

Breathing with Your Whole Body

Let your body relax either lying prone in savasana or standing up in the mountain pose. With each inhale, imagine that the air is spreading throughout your body, all the way down to your toes. With each exhale, imagine that tensions are flowing out. You may find it helpful to imagine that the air coming in is light-colored and bright and the air going out is murky and dark. Allow your muscles to release and permit tensions to ease in response.

Gentle Yoga Routine to Activate Your Nervous System

When feeling depressed, you may not feel like being active. This series of bends—first forward, then back, then sideways—will raise the energy throughout your body. And you can do it from the comfort of your chair or seated on the floor. Don't push beyond what is comfortable. What is most important is that you coordinate your movements, breathing, and mental focus. Once your energy is raised, perform the movements from a standing mountain pose.

Begin by finding your balance point, using the exercise to discover your balance from a seated position as described in Chapter 6, in the section, "Finding Your Balanced Sitting Position on page 54. After a minute or so of balanced sitting, bring your hands together, palms touching. Perform several soft breaths. When you feel calm and ready to start, exhale completely. Then, begin inhaling as you circle your arms out and up above your head until your palms touch each other, extended above your head. Bend backward as you look up and complete a slow inhalation. Hold for a moment and then breathe out and in again.

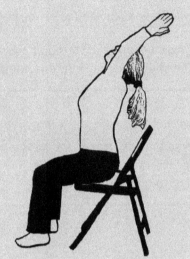

FIGURE 14.3 Chair Sitting Back Bend

Breathe out slowly as you bend forward from the waist. Tuck your head between your arms as you exhale. Keep your back straight for as long as possible as you lower your upper body down. Go only as far as you can. Let your arms hang down. Hold this position and breathe comfortably in and out several times. Slowly return to the upright seated position. Breathe gently.

FIGURE 14.4 Chair Sitting Forward Bend

Now extend your arms out sideways to shoulder height, and inhale. Rotate your left hand down to lightly grasp the side of your chair as your right arm comes overhead, until it is pointing straight up. Slowly bend toward the left, keeping your arm stretched overhead as you continue to bend sideways. From this position, relax your neck muscles and any other muscles that are not involved in this stretch and breathe comfortably. Slowly straighten as you inhale again and return to the starting position. Repeat the same motion on the other side.

Finally, come back to the center as you sit upright with your hands together, palms touching. Breathe in and out for several minutes as you pay attention mindfully to your body. Do you feel energized?

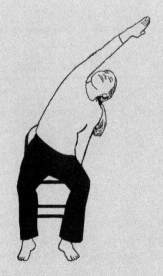

FIGURE 14.5 Chair Sitting Triangle

Clearing Your Chakras Meditation

When you are depressed, the prana in your chakras is lowered. Certain chakras may even be blocked. Clearing your chakras of blockages can help to revitalize you and restore your energy. With your energy flowing better, feelings of well-being arise that will be helpful for altering your general depressive pattern.

Sit cross-legged on a pillow on the floor in an easy pose, and breathe gently for several minutes. If you are uncomfortable on the floor, sit on a straight-backed chair. (See Figure 5.3 to review the location of each chakra.)

1. *Now focus on your root chakra, located at the base of your spine, and visualize red energy swirling around. Feel your connection to the ground as you concentrate on your stable foundation. Draw strength from the ground as you visualize the red energy flowing upward.*

2. *Let the energy rise up and imagine that it is turning orange as it swirls around your sacral chakra, just below your navel. Feel your creative energies flowing as you allow your playful and spontaneous nature to be expressed.*

3. *Now, move your energy up to your solar plexus and visualize yellow energy spinning around. Feel your confidence grow as this bright yellow energy fills you here, moving freely around. You can feel your sense of self, of who you are, and see yourself living up to your highest potential.*

4. *Allow the energy to move up into your heart. Imagine the color turning green as it rotates around your heart center, evoking feelings of love and compassion. You might think of someone you love or a general feeling of caring for humanity. Let the energy move and swirl around, filling your heart chakra.*

5. *Visualize your energy moving up to the base of your throat, becoming a beautiful turquoise blue. Imagine your capacity to express yourself as you truly are. Visualize yourself taking responsibility for your life, shaping it as you would like.*

6. *Imagine energy moving up into your forehead, becoming deep indigo, in the third eye chakra, the seat of wisdom. As you picture this dark blue energy circling, your inner vision clears. Listen to your intuition and allow understanding to clarify and grow.*

7. *Allow energy to rise up to the top of your head, into your crown chakra, becoming royal purple colored, pure, as you sense your spiritual nature. Feel your connection with the greater cosmos, drawing on its ineffability for your inspiration. Breathe and relax as you feel energy flowing throughout your body, aglow like a rainbow, with positive potential available to you now.*

MINDFULNESS TO TRANSFORM NEGATIVE THINKING

If you are feeling depressed, you may find yourself entangled in negative thoughts. This ancient Sufi story offers a new way to think about negative thinking.

Who Can Say If It's Good or It's Bad

Once upon a time, an unhappy farmer went to the village master to lament about his plight. He complained, "My farm is failing. Everything is terrible! What should I do?"

The master replied mysteriously, "Who can say if it's good or it's bad."

The farmer returned to his farm somewhat puzzled. That night a wild stallion appeared on his farm. The farmer couldn't believe his luck! He was overjoyed! He captured the stallion and harnessed it for work. He took all his money and invested in seeds, expecting that at last, with the help of this horse, he would be able to make great profits. Then he returned to the master. Grinning as he spoke, he told the master, "I'm overjoyed that the stallion had come! Now I can plow twice as many fields." He fully expected the master to agree.

But the master simply replied, "Who can say if it's good or it's bad."

The farmer returned to his farm even more puzzled than the last time. He planted the seeds and worked very hard during the following weeks. The plants grew well. He looked forward to harvesting the crops soon. Then, one night, the stallion disappeared. The farmer was devastated! He had spent his last dollar on the seeds. All the fruits and vegetables would rot without the horse to help him harvest. He returned to the master heartbroken over the loss of the stallion.

The master replied, "Who can say if it's good or it's bad.

The farmer returned home feeling desolate. But the next morning, to his great surprise and joy, the stallion returned and brought with him a mare. Now the farmer was ecstatic! Not only would he have plenty of labor from both horses, he would also be assured of his future because there would probably be more horses from them in the future. He rushed to the master to tell him the wonderful news and receive the master's blessing.

Instead, the master replied, "Who can say if it's good or it's bad."

The next day, the farmer's eldest and strongest son was riding the stallion, harvesting the crop. Suddenly the stallion reared and threw the son off, severely injuring his back. Now the farmer was very upset. His son, the best worker, would have to rest in bed for months. He told the master that his grief was boundless.

Again, the master replied, "Who can say if it's good or it's bad."

As it turned out, the national army came around to all the farms recruiting the firstborn son of every family to battle at the front lines. Because the farmer's son was injured, he did not have to go. And who can say if this was good or bad? It is possible that the son could have become a war hero and a stronger person from the experience, or perhaps he would have been killed.

When you are feeling depressed, you may despair of anything changing and feel hopeless about the future. But who can say if it's good or it's bad? What you may not realize is that you unintentionally elicit a depressed reaction in yourself, by dreading the future and worrying about the past. You may become consumed by negative thoughts that seem rational. And these thoughts can be compelling because they seem to arise from reason. If you dwell on things going or not going your way, then, like the farmer, you ride a roller coaster of emotion, up hills of exhilaration and down slopes of despair. And in a sense, when focused on feeling depressed, you are in a negative dharana! Free yourself to experience the wealth of nuances by entering an open dharana in the present moment, and you will discover fertile ground to nurture the full range of potential that is always there. Mindfulness elicits a lasting alteration in your *way* of thinking, lighting the path for clear, awake, and aware perception to shine through. Enlightenment transforms the darkness of judging itself, changing this negative pattern forever.

Opening to Change: Who Can Say If It's Good or It's Bad

Sit quietly, close your eyes, and notice your thoughts as they pass through your mind. Pay attention to what you are thinking now about the circumstances of your life. For example, you may notice that you are dwelling on something that once was said to you or perhaps ruminating over how terrible you feel.

Think of the farmer, tossed back and forth by his judgments. Then, ask yourself, "Who can say it it's good or it's bad?" You are embarking on a journey that will take you out of depression. It begins by wondering what you might learn as you answer the master's question.

Mindful of the Patterns of Thoughts Checklist

Take a step back to observe your patterns of thought. Typically, when people are depressed, their thoughts form certain kinds of patterns:

- Self-critical
- Self-castigating
- Self-blaming
- Helpless and hopeless

You may observe other patterns. Recognizing your thought patterns is a helpful step for altering your depressed mood. Here are some typical thoughts for each category. Check any of these thought patterns you may be engaging in. Make note of any others you may be telling yourself.

FIGURE 14.6 Mindful of Patterns of Thoughts Checklist

SELF-CRITICISM	Always	Sometimes	Never
I'm a failure.			
I'm wasting my life.			
I spend too much money, eat too much, sleep too much, etc.			
I'm too fat, stupid, etc.			
Other:			

SELF-CASTIGATION	Always	Sometimes	Never
I deserve all the bad things that happen to me.			
I don't deserve to be cared for/ loved.			
I don't merit feeling good.			
Other:			

SELF-BLAME	Always	Sometimes	Never
It's my fault.			
I made her/him say/do that.			
If it wasn't for me, that bad thing wouldn't have happened.			
Other:			

HELPLESS AND HOPELESS	Always	Sometimes	Never
There's nothing I can do.			
I feel helpless.			
Nothing I ever do is right.			
Other:			

Perform mindful awareness of your thoughts several times, noting down typical thoughts, until you have identified your negative thought patterns. But remember: Just observe objectively. Then, move on to the next section.

Transform Your Negative Patterns into Potential

Once you have identified typical thought patterns, instead of identifying them as terrible or bad, simply observe and trust the process. As this workbook has described throughout, mindfulness is based on the simple idea of noticing the full range of experience. So, that means not to judge your judgments! Accepting *all* your experiences allows you to notice more so that a transformation can take place.

Transforming Negativity into Potential

Now that you have begun to accept yourself as you are, can you recognize hidden potential that you might have overlooked before? Use your ability to judge for, rather than against, yourself. If there is a purpose it serves, try to find a way to achieve the better intention, without harm or threat to you or others.

For example, sustaining your negativity probably required you to be somewhat strong-willed. And passing judgment on things engages your critical intelligence. Anger often contains an impulse toward constructive aggression and strength that can serve as a source for motivation to accomplish things in the real world. Sadness may become an expression of sensitivity, empathy, and caring. One depressed client learned to appreciate her sadness because it lent depth and compassion to her artwork. Another learned to appreciate his aggression, which he moderated through meditative awareness, motivating him to follow through on projects. Consider this: Does your negativity do something positive for you? That may be why it is hard for you to let it go.

Look for the Positive Meditation

Sit or lie down to meditate when you are feeling negative, (or angry or sad). Contemplate what your negativity (or anger or sadness) does for you. In what way might it be helpful to you? As you come to recognize some of your hidden strengths, perseverance, or compassion, you will find it easier to wholeheartedly accept all of your feelings.

Do Unto Yourself at Least as You Would Do Unto Others

When you struggle, extend compassion for yourself, just as you would for someone else who is suffering. Recall when you gave comfort to someone. Can you extend that kind of comfort to yourself now, even when feeling low? You are okay. Your feelings matter. Your depth of feeling is part of you. Breathe, relax, and let be.

Self-Acceptance Now

Return to meditation. Become mindful of yourself in this present moment. Accept the full range of your experience: the temperature of your skin, the tonus of your muscles, the feeling of your heartbeat, the air flowing in and out as you breathe, and your emotions and thoughts. Can you accept your experiencing as it flows?

NURTURING HAPPINESS

Excessive negativity leads to uncomfortable feelings. But the opposite is also true: You can nurture happiness and well-being. The Dalai Lama encourages people to cultivate positive moods. "All of the virtuous states of mind—compassion, tolerance, forgiveness, caring, and so on. . .cannot co-exist with ill feelings or negative states of mind" (Dalai Lama, 1998). Your mood is a response to your nervous system, and so another way to alter depression is to cultivate calm and balance in your nervous system, which in turn influences your thoughts and emotions, and thereby lifts your depressed mood.

Discovering Enjoyment Through Simple Actions: Mindful Walking

You may have been overlooking the simple pleasures of life for a long time, but now is a good time to begin appreciating your life again. Mindful walking is an easy practice that can turn the tides. You can easily integrate mindful walking into your daily routine by taking a five- or ten-minute walk outdoors or even around the house. If you do not have a regular exercise routine, you can certainly add some exercise with a minute or two of mindful walking. You can vary the pace, but usually mindful walking begins with a slow pace.

We encourage you to apply mindfulness to other simple actions you perform, such as washing the car or folding laundry. Any action offers an opportunity to be mindful. You may be surprised to discover that a positive mood is a regular possibility for you now.

Step out with one foot, placing your heel down first and rolling onto your toe as you swing your opposite arm forward with the step. Walk very slowly, aware of each step, heel to toe, arms swinging naturally in this way, focused on the sensation of your foot as it meets the floor, your arms as they swing by your sides, the regular shift of balance, and breathing in tune with each step. Keep your attention focused only on walking. If your mind wanders, gently bring it back to your walking as soon as you notice. Continue walking, comfortably aware. Do you feel tension levels lower?

For a variation, walk more quickly, keeping your attention focused on walking as you do. Breathe comfortably and keep your movements relaxed and loose. When you have finished walking, stand for a few minutes in the mountain pose, breathe comfortably, and mindfully pay attention to standing. Open your eyes and stretch. Do you feel refreshed and at peace?

Engaging in Meaningful Actions

Yoga and mindfulness encourage linking your mind, body, and spirit together for full involvement in everything you do. As you begin to feel more energy and resolve some of your negative patterns, you will feel the stirrings to do more. These exercises will guide you in directing your energies outward toward the world where you can find satisfaction and fulfillment.

You learn about yourself through the meaningful activities that you engage in. It is important to give yourself time to engage in such activities. They might be a hobby or a career-oriented action. But how do you know what to pursue? The seeds of your interests and talents were planted long ago. This exercise will link to your whole being, past and future, before and after being depressed.

Looking Back Exercise

What did you like doing as a child? Were you happiest with a box of crayons and paper? Or maybe you liked running around for hours? Or did you enjoy playing with building blocks?

Now think of a way to do something like that now. For example, we enjoyed creating "things to do" books and family newspapers as children. Now we find fulfillment in writing books, such as this workbook! Perhaps your love of coloring can be expressed now as painting, drawing, or calligraphy. Maybe your enjoyment of running around could be transferred to jogging or long-distance walking. And the childhood fun with blocks might be expressed by doing a craft such as woodworking or projects around the house. Give yourself some time to pursue one of your youthful interests in the present context. You may find that you have ability there and enjoy doing it. And these early interests lead you to new meaningful activities to fill out your life.

Looking Forward Exercise

What would you like to do in a future in which you are not depressed? How would you go about it? Visualize yourself feeling comfortable with yourself. What do you want to do? Once you identify that thing, try doing it. Enjoy how you feel now. Your imagined future beyond depression comes from the capacities and talents you have now. Nurture them and you will enjoy the fruits!

REFINE YOUR ACTION WITH JOURNALING

Everything you do can confirm the intent of yoga and mindfulness: to perform wholeheartedly, truly, and fully. You can work on enhancing your actions in the world by going through the yamas and niyamas as instructed in Chapter 4. Answer the questions there in terms of the action you are involved in. For example, suppose you chose woodworking. Here is a chart with questions to ask yourself as you pursue this craft. Please feel free to adapt these questions to whatever activity you are doing.

Yamas For Action

1. Ahimsa, nonharming
   - Are you taking the necessary safeguards, such as wearing a protective mask, wearing gloves when applying finishes, and using dust collection when cutting?

2. Satya, not lying
   - Can you work patiently and carefully to make your wood flat and "true" and have your joinery fit exactly? You will find truth in an exact joint fitting, 90 degrees, without gaps. Aiming for the truth in whatever you do will raise the quality of your actions.

3. Asteya, not stealing
   - Acquire your materials and tools honestly. Make your own designs or give credit where it is due if you use a design from a book or plans. Ultimately it will become a blending of your unique talents with the contributions of other experts.

4. Brahmacharya, moderation and restraint
   - Can you be patient and take the time needed to do the job well? Often we are tempted to rush and then things don't come out well. If you are feeling impatient and tempted to rush, pause and meditate. Return to it later, with care and restraint. You will not be disappointed!

5. Aparigraha, nonattachment
   - Can you put your creation out into the world without attachment? Once you have created something, it is part of the world. Of course, you are the creator, but you will get great satisfaction if you can allow others to share in enjoying your work too.

Niyamas for Action

1. Shaucha, purity
   - Can you refine your actions to move smoothly and well? So, when performing the movements of your craft, try to do them smoothly. If you are a woodworker, when you are planing wood, make a long, smooth motion. Keep your body and mind focused on the action, clear and in the moment of what you do while you do it. Feel the motion and breathe in and out with it, as if using the tool is just an extension of your hand and arm. The tool is part of you. This applies to knitting or other simple crafts as well.

2. Santosha, contentment
   - Can you find satisfaction and contentment in actions themselves as you do them? Keep your eye on what you are doing now rather than worrying about how it will come out, how good it will be.

3. Tapas, austerity
   - Don't add anything extra to what you are doing. Use just the right tools and no more. Don't be carried away by the allure of fancy tools or materials that are beyond your budget. Keep the lines clean, the designs exact.

4. Pranitara, self-study
   - Do you have the humility to learn whatever you need to enhance your skills? Take a class, watch a teaching video, or consult an expert to expand your knowledge. The wise person knows what he or she knows not!

5. Ishvara pranidana, devotion to higher values
   - Can you keep the higher virtues of your craft in mind: beauty, truth, and skill? Meditate on these qualities and let them become part of your being.

Gratitude Meditation

Think about something you are grateful for in your life. You might pick one of the items from your journaling as your topic for meditation, or perhaps something new has occurred to you. Sit quietly and meditate on what you are grateful for. Let your gratitude grow as you keep your attention on being grateful.

Review your gratitude list regularly and perform a meditation for each item on your list. Try doing the meditation for several minutes when you first awaken and several minutes just before sleep. Return to this meditation often, especially if you find your thoughts becoming negative.

Expanding Your Compassion Meditation

Sit in meditation for several minutes. Then allow yourself to feel compassion for someone you care about. Feel the warmth of caring spread through you. Next, let your compassion move out to someone you know more peripherally, an acquaintance, the people next door, or someone at work. Now feel compassion for everyone who lives in your town or city, as fellow citizens who share a certain geography and culture. Expand outward to include the entire country, then the world, and finally all living beings. Let the glow of compassion spread through you as you sit calmly now.

POSITIVE JOURNALING

Making some of your discoveries part of you may take time. Keep a journal and record some of your positive reflections, just as you may have been in the habit of only noting down things that upset you. Here are some guidelines for positive journaling to help you continue to nurture being happy.

1. Gratitude List: List several things you are grateful for in your life. You might think that you have nothing to feel thankful about in your life. But, once you start looking, you may be surprised to find that you have many things to feel grateful for. Your gratitude could come from a simple pleasure in eating a delicious cookie, from seeing a beautiful bird fly by, or even from the simple pleasure of sitting in the shade of a large tree on a warm, sunny day. You might feel grateful for certain people in your life, the education you have had, or a pet that you love. Let yourself be open to searching for these things, and you will be surprised how many you can find.

2. Think of an important trait about yourself that you don't like.
   a. Ask yourself, "What does it do to me?" and note that down.
   b. Then ask, "What does it do for me?" and note that down.

3. Acceptance: Note down ways you can accept and appreciate all of your different qualities.

4. Complete items 2 and 3 with as many qualities of your personality that seem important to you. Work on finding ways to appreciate who you are and making those qualities work for you.

CHAPTER 15

Ending Substance Abuse and Finding Fulfillment

For one whose thought is tranquil, mastery extends from the
most minute particle to the vast expanse.
—Patañjali's Yoga Sutras translated by Miller, 1995

IN THIS CHAPTER

- Study a neuroscience perspective on substance abuse
- Educate yourself about your addiction
- Rewire your nervous system for healthy reward
- Train in mindfulness techniques to overcome cravings
- Learn yoga and mindfulness methods to ease withdrawal
- Engage ways to maintain your recovery and foster your potential

INTRODUCTION

Addiction is a mind-brain-body problem, and so treating it with a therapy that alters all three will be most effective. If you are dependent on a substance, your mind is focused on the substance. Your brain is rewired around the substance, helping to explain why most of your pleasure comes from engaging in your habit. In addition, you feel discomfort and even pain in your body if you stop taking the substance. The combination of pleasure from using and pain from withdrawal along with the way your brain has been rewired, makes substance abuse difficult to overcome. Yoga and mindfulness address all these problems on multiple levels: mind, brain, body, and spirit. You change your mind's focus, rewire your brain's pathways, soothe your body's discomforts, and draw on your spiritual nature to help you overcome the pull of addiction.

The Woman Who Learned to Relax on Her Own

Jean came to us to give up smoking. She knew it was bad for her. Her husband wanted her to quit, and she worried about setting a bad example for her children. Nonetheless, she was unable to give it up.

We taught her meditative hypnosis. During one session, she was meditating deeply with her body visibly relaxed. Suddenly, she opened her eyes and sat bolt upright saying, "I can't do this!" We were surprised and asked her, "Why?" She explained with a strong sense of certainty in her voice, "I realized that the only time I relax is when I sit down and have a cigarette. If I give up cigarettes, I will have to give up relaxing! I can't do that!" Now that she was aware of what she was really feeling and doing, we were able to guide her in learning how to relax without a cigarette. She had no problem letting go of smoking and enjoying her life more fully, relaxed, and comfortable!

NEUROSCIENCE OF ADDICTION

The neuroscience of addiction explains why it can be so difficult to overcome a drug habit. Drug-taking behavior alters the reward pathway of the brain. We are wired to seek pleasurable experiences. The reward pathway begins in the midbrain, projects to the forebrain, and then goes back to the midbrain. This pathway is involved in the normal feelings of pleasure for behaviors that are necessary for survival such as eating, drinking, and sex. When you engage in one of these activities, dopamine is released, and you feel pleasure. The powerful experience of pleasure you get from taking a drug is due to how it activates your reward pathway to release dopamine.

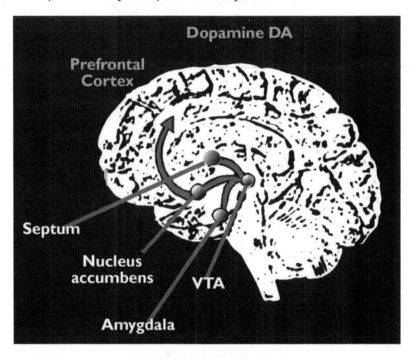

FIGURE 15.1 Reward Pathway

There are different kinds of addictive drugs that have varied specific actions and effects, but they all share in the same general impact they have on the brain through the reward pathway. The use of an addictive substance brings about a strong sense of pleasure as the substance enters the bloodstream and brain, resulting in an intense craving to repeat the experience. Normally, the blood-brain barrier prevents the passage of molecules into the brain, keeping the nervous system stable. But many drugs, including pharmacological medications, penetrate the blood-brain barrier, altering the balance of neurotransmitters. Nicotine, alcohol, cocaine, barbiturates, and opiates can easily cross the blood-brain barrier, which is why these drugs have such a powerful impact on users.

But when you use drugs regularly, you expend all the pleasure at once, which is like taking the foot off the brakes, thereby releasing more dopamine. The drug dramatically alters the brain's activity all the way down to the synapses between neurons, such that you may find little joy in anything but your drug.

Yoga and mindfulness rewire the reward pathway back to normal. Mindfulness meditation can help you overcome your cravings by altering the pleasure-pain struggle. In addition, yoga methods help alleviate the physical discomforts that accompany withdrawal. And through your own practice, you discover pleasure, satisfaction, and lasting well-being arising from your inner resources.

Information Box

PRECAUTION: Whenever you undergo withdrawal from an addictive drug, you should be medically monitored. Never try to do it alone. Practice the yoga and mindfulness exercises included in this chapter and throughout this book as you undergo treatment at a hospital or drug treatment center or with a therapist. Licensed medical practitioners can offer you proper care throughout the process.

LEARN ABOUT YOUR ADDICTION WITH MINDFUL JOURNALING

According to yoga tradition, the body is the temple of the soul, the breath is the lord of the mind, and the mind is the sovereign of the senses. Any yoga and mindfulness approach to overcoming substance abuse involves cultivating your mind and breathing to help you control your senses. Your body heals as you gain self-knowledge of your physical, mental, and spiritual being.

The flywheel of habit turns, and you may find yourself stuck in patterns that are harmful to you without being aware of it. The yamas and niyamas provide some guidelines that can help you survey your current lifestyle and get back in touch. Review Chapter 4 on the yamas and niyamas. Use your journal to help you observe and record your experience. But remember: Don't judge yourself, turning these into another set of moral values. Observe and exercise restraint where possible, with the faith that you are engaged in a positive process. Use your journal to reflect on these issues as you inspire recovery and fulfillment.

Yama Reflection

Begin with the yamas to help you question and even stop engaging in some of the patterns that have led to where you are now.

1. Ahimsa, compassion and nonharming
   - List ways you may be harming yourself and others
   - How can you practice nonharming, not just in actions, but also in attitudes and thoughts?

2. Satya, not Lying
   - List some ways you might be deceiving yourself about your drug use. For example, when we asked our client Nicky about how often she used drugs she answered in naïve honesty, "Oh, not much at all. Well, I smoke a little pot when I get up, then I have a six-pack or so of beer during the day. I might smoke again before I go out at night, and then, well, when I'm partying (which I do four to five times a week), I like to use a little speed to keep me going, or I might drop some acid. But, I don't really use drugs, and I could stop taking the little bit that I do any time I want to. I just don't feel like it." She was sincere, unaware of her self-deception. She honestly hadn't faced that her life revolved around a regular habitual pattern. She didn't really use drugs. They used her.
   - Educate yourself about the truth regarding regular alcohol and drug use. Information about the harmful effects of drugs is readily available on the Internet as well as other places, such as treatment programs (e.g., Narcotics Anonymous).
   - Write down some ways you could look at things more realistically and truthfully about the substance(s) you use. Then free yourself to choose.

3. Asteya, not stealing
   - Do you want to have something that doesn't really belong to you or that you haven't earned? Sometimes people use drugs as a shortcut. For example, one client said, "I feel at my best: energetic, confident, and competent, when I'm high." He used amphetamines regularly, and although he felt self-assured when using, the drug was

killing him. Ingesting the drug for confidence and energy was turning him away from his own inner resources, leaving him feeling depleted and ill when the drug wore off. With the support of therapy, he turned toward the true source of confidence and competence, the wellspring within him.

- List some of the things you want out of life. Note ways to truly achieve these goals from your own resources (e.g., getting schooling or training, becoming more fit, or developing a talent).
- Are there ways you are relying on other people or drugs instead of relying on your own abilities?
- List how you can give rather than take.

4. Brahmacharya, restraint
   - Drug use often involves a valuing of being "high." Write down your thoughts about what it means to feel high. For example, does it symbolize freedom?
     □ If so, question whether you are truly free, since drug use comes with a heavy price: dependency.
     □ List ways you have had a natural high without drugs.
       ■ Have you experienced well-being following yoga and mindfulness practice?
       ■ Have you felt a similar glow after sharing closeness with a significant other or from creating something yourself?
   - As you reread your thoughts about these possibilities, resolve to learn the skills you need to achieve higher consciousness without drugs.

5. Aparigraha, nongrasping
   - Dependence on drugs is a kind of attachment. You can develop detachment to resist the pushes and pulls of dependency.
     □ Note when you have been detached from something, able to let something go, without relying on anything outside of yourself, even a small thing.
   - Observe ways that you are putting the source for your well-being outside of yourself rather than within.
   - List your strengths, ways that you can facilitate your own capacities. Ask significant others to list your strengths and capacities.

Niyama Reflection

Niyamas offer positive values to give you the strength to flourish.

1. Shaucha, purity
   - Shaucha can be your inspiration to do what you can to become healthy in body, mind, and spirit. Withdrawing carefully under medical supervision is one aspect of recovery, but you can prepare yourself by caring for your body with healthy eating and adequate sleep. Practice the breathing, postures, and meditations regularly.
   - Schedule a brief, daily yoga and mindfulness session.
   - Look up nutrition on the Internet or at the library. Plan a healthy day's meals you can imagine integrating into your eating routine.

2. Santosha, contentment
   - Note the things you like about your life as it is now. Even though you probably have much you would like to change, find a few things that you feel good about.
   - Practice mindfulness for one minute and appreciate the quiet.

3. Tapas, austerity
   - You can draw on *tapas* to help you handle the challenges ahead. We all have a superhero in us, even if it's tucked away.
   - List a time or times when you endured something tough.
   - Note what it would be like to be strong and capable now.

4. Svadhyaya, self-education
   - What would you like to do with your life?
   - List some of your interests.

- Learn more about each of these interests.
    - ☐ Borrow books from the library on one of these topics.
    - ☐ Talk to people whom you admire.
    - ☐ Discuss your interests with people who are involved in them.
    - ☐ Search the Internet.
    - ☐ Educate yourself, delve deeply, and follow up on your curiosity.
5. Ishvara pranidhana, discover the divine within
    - What inspires you?
    - Put yourself into an inspirational situation, for example:
        - ☐ Admire a sunset.
        - ☐ Take a walk in nature.
        - ☐ Read an inspiring book.
        - ☐ Be with young children.
        - ☐ Watch an inspirational movie.
    - How can you open yourself to the spiritual dimension?
    - Write about times when you have felt spiritual.

CHART YOUR HABIT

FIGURE 15.2 Chart Your Drug Use for One Week

	Use of substance	What are you thinking and feeling?	What were you doing right before?
Monday morning midday evening			
Tuesday morning midday evening			
Wednesday morning midday evening			
Thursday morning midday evening			
Friday morning midday evening			
Saturday morning midday evening			
Sunday morning midday evening			

REWIRE YOUR REWARD PATHWAY AWAY FROM DRUGS

If you have been abusing drugs or alcohol, your dopamine has been depleted, which helps to explain why you may feel less enjoyment in life. Research on the yoga technique, yoga nidra, has been shown to increase dopamine release. A group of researchers in Denmark measured subjects using two PET scans for two conditions. In the first condition, participants turned their attention to speech with their eyes closed, and in the second condition, they performed yoga nidra meditations. During the meditation condition, dopamine release increased by 65% (Kjaer, Bertelsen, Piccini, Brooks, Alving, & Lou, 2002).

Yoga Nidra Meditation

You can perform yoga nidra meditation to become calm, bring balance to your nervous system, and increase the release of dopamine, thereby, giving you a pleasurable experience without resorting to your chemical substance. Regular practice can put you on the path to rewiring your reward pathway away from your substance and back to healthy reward.

You might find that your body temperature will lower slightly as you lie still. To keep your body temperature stable, cover yourself with a light blanket before beginning yoga nidra meditation.

Lie down on your back in savasana. If you back is sore, place a pillow under your legs behind your knees to relax your lower back. Breathe comfortably in and out for several minutes and allow your breathing to relax. Now, focus your attention on your right foot. Allow it to relax as completely as possible. Then, move your attention up through your leg to your knee, relaxing these areas. Continue moving your attention all the way up to your thigh and then to your hip, relaxing all the muscles as you go. Now, become aware of your entire leg, letting it relax completely. Next, focus attention on your left foot and let your attention travel up to your hip, relaxing as you go. Now, move up though your whole body, part by part, relaxing as you go. Notice your torso area, front and back, waist, chest, lower to middle to upper back, right hand, right arm, right shoulder, then focus on your left side in a similar manner up your neck, throat, face, and finally to the top of your head. When you have finished, breathe comfortably as you notice your entire body, relaxed and at ease. Finally, feel your body as it meets the surface you lie on. Then extend the range of your awareness to include the room you are in. When you feel ready, open your eyes and stretch, relaxed and refreshed from your pleasurable yoga nidra experience. Practice this meditation daily, to help your nervous system regain its natural capacity to enjoy life, without the help of external stimulants or depressants.

Stabilize Your Breath

Your breathing tends to reflect your inner state, and so by stabilizing your breathing you can literally stabilize your entire nervous system.

Sit in the pelvic pose or the easy pose, with your back held relatively straight. Perform several relaxed, complete breaths. Next, inhale naturally, hold for three counts, and then exhale completely. When you get to the bottom of your exhale, gently draw in your stomach muscles and hold for three counts. Inhale slowly, letting the air completely fill your lungs and expand your stomach muscles. Perform the pattern three times and then perform three comfortable complete breaths. Repeat the pattern for several minutes. When you are ready, sit quietly, relaxing your breathing.

MODERATE IMPULSES AND STRENGTHEN RESOLVE

You may be bothered by cravings and impulses, thinking you can't control them. But that very thought may be aggravating the problem. Consider this: Perhaps your tolerance for pain should expand. We often think of directing our efforts toward lessening pain or getting rid of it. But to be able to truly overcome discomfort, you need to change your approach to it. Mindfulness offers a different tool for control of uncomfortable cravings.

Pursuing pleasure and avoiding pain puts you on a roller coaster. Mindfulness helps you go beyond this pleasure-pain cycle. Grounded in the present moment, you become detached from your typical discomforts and open up to something new. When working on cravings, do this series of meditations several times a day. Stay with it.

This kind of personal work, when coupled with appropriate professional care, can help you to master your situation and yourself.

1. Detaching from Cravings

When you experience craving, feeling as if something is missing and you want to fill a void, turn your mindful eye from inside to outside. Look around the room in which you are sitting. What do you see? Notice the lighting, the colors, and any textures and shapes. Are there other people there? Turn your attention to what other people are doing. Don't judge them—just as you shouldn't judge yourself. You may be surprised to notice interesting qualities that you have missed. Allow your attention to remain focused on your environment, experiencing without evaluating. Breathe comfortably as you notice.

2. Tolerating Cravings

After you have become mindful of your environment, turn your mindful attention inward as you relax your breathing and let go of any unnecessary tensions. Observe what you are experiencing now, but don't label what you notice, simply watch. Tolerate and accept your feelings just as an experience. Notice the qualities of the sensations. If the feelings become too intense, shift your attention outward again. Go back and forth, inward and outward, while you relax as much as possible. Soon your craving will begin to alter somewhat. You may even feel that it has less of a pull on you.

3. Questioning Cravings

Question why you really need this habit so much. Perhaps you have defined yourself as this or that type of person who needs it, but remember, that in your deeper, true nature, you were not born with this need. You developed it through your own thoughts and experiences. You can become detached from the craving, the need, through your own inner renunciation.

EASE YOUR WITHDRAWAL

When you feel ready to withdraw, seek medical assistance to ensure that you go through the process safely. You can use your yoga and mindfulness skills to ease your withdrawal. Without realizing it, you may be adding to your pain and discomfort by your interpretations. You feel uncomfortable and then think, "I can't stand it, it's awful, terrible," or perhaps telling yourself that your personal suffering is unique and far worse than anyone else. But with mindful awareness, you subtract the evaluative part of your experience. Research has found that negative evaluation of pain, processed in the cingulate gyrus, literally intensifies your pain. So, learning to mindfully accept what you are feeling, even if it hurts, will lower your pain experience and increase your pain tolerance. You can influence your discomforts much more than you might believe possible, and these next exercises show you how. You can also use the meditations to overcome cravings.

1. Dharana Meditation to Transform Discomfort

The discomfort associated with withdrawal is often felt as an overwhelming experience, something that hurts you. But in truth, pain is a combination of sensations and cognitive appraisal. By learning to separate these parts and distinguish them, the sensations become manageable and the interpretation can alter. With willingness and practice, you can do it!

Warm up session: Do this exercise when you are feeling only a slight discomfort. As your skills improve, you will be able to apply this meditation to strong cravings or pains. Notice the sensory component of the discomfort you are feeling. Focus on its qualities: Is it hot or cold, sharp or dull, or anything else? Do you feel the discomfort as an intermittent pulse with spaces between, or is it a continuous wave?

Pay particularly close attention to the spaces between, the times when the sensation is not there. What are the qualities of these moments, when there is no discomfort or less intensity? Can you remain objective, simply attending to it, like data to be observed? When you have been able to sustain attention to the sensations, move on to the next exercise.

2. Withdrawing from Discomfort

Now that you have learned to experience the elements of the uncomfortable sensation without distinguishing the sensation as pleasant or unpleasant, apply pratyahara to withdraw from these sensations, however you experience them. Begin by attending to the strongest, most intense sensations, then turn your attention to the subtler ones, then to spaces between the sensations, and eventually to moments without sensation. Allow the relief from lulls in pain to spill over into the moments of intense sensations, softening them a bit. Let the feeling of calm that you develop spread. As it becomes deeper and stronger, the sensations may become milder and easier to handle. Keep breathing comfortably and allow as much relaxation as possible.

3. Meditate on Something Else

You may find yourself getting fatigued from meditations 1 and 2. Learning how to concentrate your attention on something else is a tried and true way to lessen the experience of pain and discomfort and give you some rest. You have had moments when you became spontaneously absorbed in something interesting. It might have been great music, a fascinating book, an intriguing movie, or being deeply involved with others. Although this exercise guides in focusing attention fully on music, please feel free to choose what fascinates you.

Pick something that you can enjoy easily. Listen to a piece of instrumental music you find soothing. Listen carefully to the melody one time through. Play the music again and listen to the background sounds, perhaps a subtle rhythm, or a secondary thread that runs through the music. Play it a third time and listen only to the pauses between notes, the quietest sounds, the empty moments between. Play it one more time and listen to everything together. In the union of melody, background sounds, and spaces between you can find the full enjoyment of the music. Finally, simply sit quietly and allow listening, open and absorbed in the experience. You may hear the music as you never have before, and enjoy it fully. With practice, you can become absorbed in whatever you choose to focus your attention on.

Try applying this exercise to other sensory experiences, such as the sweet aroma of a rose, the taste of a ripe piece of fruit, or the enjoyment of viewing a beautiful art object. Keep your attention focused. Seek enjoyment in the experience itself. You may be pleased to find that the discomfort vanishes.

SAMYAMA ON MUSIC: FINDING PLEASURE WITHOUT DRUGS

Many drug users are simply seeking enjoyment, and yet they are continually frustrated by their addiction, which is not a source of true happiness. You can give up drugs without having to give up enjoyment, like our client Jean. Samyama practice develops your sense of well-being independent of drug use. True happiness comes from within, without the need for anything outside. As the great Zen Master Lin-Chi said many years ago, "Nothing is missing! You have everything you need." We offer this exercise for focusing on music, but if this is not what interests you, direct your attention to something else that does interest you, such as fine art or movement.

Sit comfortably in the easy pose (see Figure 6.11). Play your favorite music as you listen intensely with your eyes closed. Develop dharana focus on the sounds and the qualities. Allow yourself to become completely engrossed in the music, in dhyana meditation, to be in the groove (see Chapter 9, the exercise "Dhyana Meditation on Music" on page 73). Keeping all your attention on the music, let yourself dance to the beat if you feel so moved. Allow everything else to disappear for a few minutes. You are one with the music, lost in the moment. When the music is finished, sit for several minutes and experience the resonance of well-being. You can evoke this pleasurable experience whenever you choose. Your ability will grow stronger with practice.

MAINTAIN YOUR RECOVERY

Maintaining the process involves daily practice. The more frequently you practice, the easier your recovery will be. Create a daily routine of postures and meditation. We offer some simple routines here, but please feel free to incorporate any of the yoga and mindfulness practices you have found most helpful.

Open Your Energy Chakra Meditation

Overcoming dependence on a substance requires you to use everything you have to conquer the pull of the drug's powerful effects on your mind and brain. You can sustain your recovery by enlisting all of your capacities to help you. This meditation reverses the usual order of chakra meditations, to open you to receive energy, encourage its flow, and allow smooth communication within, linking your resources from mind, body, and spirit. With everything working together, you can achieve your goals! (Refer to Figure 5.3 for the location of the chakras.)

- *Sit cross-legged on a pillow or on a chair. Close your eyes and breathe in gently, hold for a few seconds, and then breathe out for a minute or so.*
- *Open the flow of your energy by focusing your attention on the crown chakra, at the top of your head. Visualize energy flowing in as the energy circles around the top of your head.*
- *Breathe comfortably as you imagine that this moving energy begins to flow downward into the brow chakra at your forehead. Here, the power of your mind is activated, stimulating your mental energy to help you with clear thinking and deeper understanding. Imagine the energy circling around your forehead as your mental vision becomes clearer and clearer.*
- *Allow all that energy to move down into your throat chakra. The energy circles around as you enhance the link between your mind and body as they work together. Your mind can communicate unimpeded with your body, and your body can send signals that are heard by your mind, with a smooth back and forth flow of energy between your mind and body.*
- *Once more, notice your breathing, in and out, and then allow your energy to sink lower into the heart chakra. Here you can open your heart to emotions of love and compassion as you follow the energy swirling around in the center of your chest. Your emotional capacities can animate your mind and body, allowing you to empathize sensitively with others.*
- *Breathe, relax, and continue to send the energy down to the solar plexus chakra, the energy center of your body. As you visualize the energy circling around, you can feel a strong sense of who you are in this moment. As you sense your mind, body, and emotions working together, you can experience confidence that you can take charge of your life and direct it toward health and happiness.*
- *Breathe, relax, and allow your energy to flow down to the sacral chakra located below your navel. Imagine it spinning around, fostering joy in living each moment as you travel your path. You can feel your creativity, your sense of enjoyment, which you can bring about without having to rely on anything outside of yourself to make it happen. As your energy flows here in your lower abdomen, you can visualize finding meaning and enjoyment in what you do.*
- *And finally, breathe, relax and let your energy sink all the way down to the root chakra at the base of your spine. Here is your connection to the earth, your source of vitality. In touch with the earth, your energy can now move from your foundation, around and around and then up again, unimpeded and free to flow wherever you send it.*

Breathing with Asanas to Stimulate Radiant Health

Breathing coordinated with movement can stimulate a healthy flow of energy. Imagine that your breathing is sending healing energy to the area you are exercising. As you breathe in, imagine that the air carries prana to that part of your body, bringing vitality to help this area develop. As you exhale, imagine that you are expelling toxins from the area. Visualize the air you breathe in as brightly colored or bright and clear. Visualize the stale air going out as dark colored and murky. Contemplate this image during posture practice. Concentrate attention on your posture while breathing, to link them.

1. *Perform a daily sun salutation (see the instructions in Chapter 11 in the section "Bottom-up Calming with the Sun Salutation" on pages 87-89 to circulate your energy and develop flexibility.*

2. *Perform the warrior series (see the instructions in Chapter 13 in the section "Embody Strength: Warrior Postures" on pages 109-110) to build strength and courage.*

3. *Enhance self-esteem and self-confidence with the standing archer pose, one of the oldest asanas of yoga practice. This posture enhances self-esteem and confidence. It builds lower and upper-body strength and improves concentration and focus.*

   a. *Place your feet wide apart as in the warrior pose. Place more of your weight on the front leg, but keep your back straight. There should be a stretch in your right upper thigh.*

   b. *Extend your arm out over your bent leg as if holding a bow and turn your head to look toward your outstretched hand, looking in that direction.*

   c. *With the other hand, perform the movements as if you are pulling back bowstrings. Your hand should be all the way past the right side of your chest.*

   d. *Breathe deeply, in and out, while holding this posture and looking steadily toward your outstretched hand.*

   e. *With every breath, keep your attention deeply focused, and feel yourself expanding as you become strong and balanced.*

   f. *Hold this position for several minutes. Then, turn and repeat on the other side.*

FIGURE 15.3 Archer Pose

FOSTER YOUR POTENTIAL

Practice yoga and mindfulness regularly to forge new habits for unifying mind and body. Breathe with movement, and keep your attention focused mindfully in the present moment. A sense of inner confidence develops. Healthy habits, daily yoga postures, regular relaxation, and mental exercises initiate a process of self-care. Take charge of your own destiny and you can transcend circumstances that seem beyond your control! Your achievements, however small they may seem, give pleasure. And even small steps will get you to your destination. This quote from Gandhi may be inspirational to you in your journey:

> *But with proper discipline, we can make ourselves into beings only a "little below the angels." He who has mastered his senses is first and foremost among men.*
> —Gandhi 1960, 143

Express Your Benevolence and Compassion

Sometimes people who get involved in harmful habits feel their life is worthless and so why not indulge in harmful habits. But if you feel your life is worthless, why not help someone else? By giving of yourself, you discover the inner goodness within. Devotion to others can be a surprising source for self-cure. The famous psychologist Alfred Adler believed that caring about and helping others is central to mental health.

It is almost impossible to exaggerate the value of an increase in social feeling. The mind improves, for intelligence is a communal function. The feeling of worth and value is heightened, giving courage, and an optimistic view. The individual feels at home in life and feels his existence to be worthwhile. . .All failures. . .are failures because they are lacking in social interest. (Adler & Deutsch, 1959)

Exchange Self-Concern for Other-Concern

Substitute compassionate, benevolent thoughts and actions for harmful ones. So, when you feel like indulging in your negative habit, try helping someone else instead. Get involved in a benevolent project or volunteer work. You might find yourself craving the positive effects brought about by your compassionate action!

Pursue Your Dreams

Each day, take one step on the path toward fulfilling your dreams. If you dream of being more organized, you might begin by cleaning out a messy drawer. You might take a larger step and enroll in a class, apply for a job, or apologize to someone to forge a better relationship. You can seek higher goals and find meaning, fulfillment, and happiness in your journey.

JOURNALING

Keep a daily journal with your thoughts, feelings, and sensations. You might choose to write at the same time every day, or you may prefer to do it randomly at different times each day. Look back after several weeks to observe trends. You may see ups and downs, which is natural. Setbacks are a normal part of the process. Extend tolerance to yourself as you would with others. Trust yourself and have faith. You can succeed!

CHARTING

FIGURE 15.4 Fostering Healthy Habits

	Monday	Tuesday	Wednesday	Thursday	Friday	Saturday	Sunday
Got a good night's sleep							
Ate three healthy, regular meals							
Pursued meaningful work							
Spent time practicing yoga and mindfulness							
Allowed time for leisure							
Spent time exercising							
Note actions that foster your comfort							
Note emotions that foster your comfort							
Other							

Guidelines for Therapists

From our acts and from our attitudes ceaseless inpouring currents of sensation come,
which help to determine from moment to moment what our inner state shall be; that is
the fundamental law of psychology, which I will therefore proceed to assume.
—James, 1917

IN THIS APPENDIX

- Bringing yoga and mindfulness into your practice
- Introducing the practices into the therapeutic hour and between sessions
- Getting your clients started
- Taking special precautions with different disorders
- Working with children
- Guiding seniors
- Lowering your stress, overcoming burnout, and enhancing clinical acumen

INTRODUCTION

More therapists are realizing that yoga and mindfulness add a helpful dimension to psychotherapy. This workbook provides a guide to yoga and mindfulness for therapy. Incorporate the exercises directly as scripts, or individualize them to fit the specific needs of your clients. Use this chapter to help optimize your use of this workbook as you integrate yoga and mindfulness into your practice.

The Man Who Rediscovered His Motivation and Sense of Purpose

A middle-aged psychologist called for an appointment. We had known him long ago, as a graduate student, and lost touch as the years passed. When he arrived for his session, he lumbered in slowly and plunked himself down on the couch. We could see that for some reason he had let himself become out of shape.

He explained that he had been trying to write his first book. When he had gotten the contract, he was excited. But now, months later, he had barely begun, and his deadline was looming. Every day he vowed to get to work on it that evening, but instead he ended up watching TV and eating junk food. The harder he tried to work on his book, the less he was able to do it. He told us, "I've gained twenty-five pounds and I don't seem to be able to get out of this pattern. I'm trapped. Please help me!"

We taught him mindfulness in the session. Then we asked him if he would be willing to do a task, with the requirement that he agree to do it before he knew what it was. We promised the task would not be harmful or dangerous in any way, and that it was related to his goal. He agreed.

His task was to climb a mountain, then stop at the top and mindfully observe the view. He replied that the task seemed inconvenient at best and that he had no idea how it could help. But, he said without trying to hide the sarcasm in his voice, "I'll do it because I promised."

He returned several weeks later, energetic, and visibly thinner. He reported that after his session, he was puzzled. He thought climbing a mountain could not possibly help him, and he certainly could be mindful anywhere; however, he knew he had agreed to do it, but felt in conflict.

One day when he was walking across the open space outside where he worked, he saw a small hill. He thought to himself, perhaps climbing that little hill would satisfy our requirement well enough. He got to the top and looked around. Suddenly, he was struck with a realization: This was exactly what he had done with his book! He had always thought his first book would represent the culmination of his unique expertise in the field that he cared deeply about. But when he was readying his proposals to publishers, he decided the original idea wouldn't sell, so instead, he opted for a popular topic that he could finish quickly with minimal effort. Now, whenever he tried to work on it, he resisted the meaningless quality of the project.

He said, "I have decided to choose the mountain!" He called his publisher and discussed adjusting the topic to his original idea. The publisher was amenable to the change, and they made the adjustments. When we saw him again, he was finding it easy to work hard on his book every day. He had returned to his healthier lifestyle and felt enthusiastic and happy again.

This example shows how people can sometimes get off track from their original inspiration. We often see therapists who have been working for many years and now feel cynical or burned out. They have lost the original excitement that drew them to the field and grown out of touch with their deeper being. In a similar respect, clients are often in despair by the time they step into your office, having lost their sense of who they are beyond problems and disturbances.

Yoga and mindfulness provide opportunities to know yourself anew. How you approach simple activities such as sitting, standing, moving, or focusing your attention on just noticing your breathing, will reveal much about your deeper nature. Conflicts may interfere with carrying out these simple tasks. We encourage you to view the exercises in this book as learning opportunities for you and your clients. In this exploratory atmosphere, you can make discoveries and access new potential that may not have been available through traditional talking therapy. By practicing yoga and mindfulness, you deal with therapeutic problems in ways that invite growth and well-being.

HOW TO BRING YOGA AND MINDFULNESS INTO YOUR PRACTICE

The power of yoga and mindfulness comes through experience. Thus, if you choose to use yoga and mindfulness with clients, we recommend experiencing it personally. Then, you will be better able to help your clients use these methods. The exercises given throughout this book offer a broad range of meditation-helpful methods for therapy.

Recognizing Individual Differences

- Everyone has different tendencies. Your client might have a different reaction than you to the exercises. For example, those you found easy might be the most difficult for your client.
- Sample each type of meditation to familiarize yourself with a broad range of methods. This experience will allow you to guide your client to those exercises that might benefit him or her most while also addressing the person's individuality.

Creating a Meditative Atmosphere

- You can add to your client's experience by creating a relaxing atmosphere in your office. Even subtle touches can suggest calm awareness to your client. Here are some tips:
  - ☐ Place two meditation pillows on the floor.
  - ☐ Add a single flower in a vase or a picture on the wall nearby that suggests meditation.
  - ☐ If you don't have enough room to add anything new, burn incense or dim the lights slightly.
- But of course, most important is your quiet mind, which invites the other to join in a meditative moment.

Introducing Yoga and Mindfulness into Group, Couples, Family, and Individual Sessions

- Integrate meditation into any format.
- If you perform group therapy, you can easily add yoga and mindfulness as part of a regular group therapy, couples, and family sessions.
  - ☐ People enjoy sharing yoga and mindfulness.
  - ☐ The wordless experience can bring a couple or family closer together.
  - ☐ You will also find that when your group shares in meditation, they will find it easier to be open and share their experiences.
  - ☐ Yoga and mindfulness practice gives tools that help clients to recognize, tolerate, and stay in touch with difficult, painful material that should be addressed.
- You may also want to offer group sessions strictly devoted to meditation for your individual clients.

Timing Yoga and Mindfulness Practice in and Between Sessions

- *Include meditation time in each session:* How long you spend doing yoga and mindfulness in your sessions with clients depends on how fully you want to integrate it into your approach. Set aside 5 to 15 minutes in each session to guide clients in their meditative practice.
- *Encourage short meditations:* In some of our talks, participants have told us that they feel frustrated when clients could not sustain meditation for 15 to 30 minutes as they did, and so gave up using it as part of therapy. We have found that it is especially difficult for people who are having emotional disturbance to sustain meditation for long periods. But they can do it for a short time. So, begin briefly, starting with a minute or less for each meditation. The feeling of mastery that the client gets from doing even a 10-second meditation will give confidence for continued efforts.
- *Begin sessions with a meditation:* You can begin with a quiet 2-minute mindfulness meditation to help the client be fully present during a session.
- *Close sessions with a meditation:* We also close sessions with a meditation to allow clients to consolidate and gather themselves before they leave. Their leaving with a sense of well-being can motivate them to return for more.
- *Encourage practice between sessions:* Practicing between sessions extends the therapeutic influence into your clients' week. You can give the client a different exercise each week, drawn from the many in this workbook. Pick what will facilitate the processes you are working on in the sessions.

□ Have clients identify a time of day for meditation and a simple posture routine that best fits their personality and schedule. First thing in the morning is good for early risers and evening practice usually suits night owls. But sometimes, contrast with the usual routine helps get around resistance.

□ Encourage clients to start with a set amount of time during which they can maintain a meditation and extend the time as they are able.

□ Encourage clients to take a mindful glance throughout the day with a 1-minute mindfulness break to observe their experiences in different circumstances.

□ Suggest that clients keep a journal of their experiences.

TIPS FOR WORKING WITH CLIENTS

- Begin with a meditative nonjudgmental attitude toward clients.
  □ Don't judge your clients' efforts.
  □ Accept their experience as unique to them.
  □ Gently lead them step-by-step toward a more calm, balanced awareness.
- When guiding clients, begin with what is easiest for them. Notice how they respond to the exercises in Chapter 3 regarding meditation tools and which they find more natural and which they find more difficult. There are many doorways into yoga and mindfulness, and when working therapeutically, it helps to start with what the client can easily master. Don't assume that your client will want to practice as you do. Don't be surprised if your client has an easier time with meditations you find difficult.

How to Introduce Yoga and Mindfulness

- Precaution: Whenever recommending a yoga posture, first ensure your client has the approval of his or her medical doctor.
- Begin with something that your clients are likely to be able to do.
  □ Direct your clients to a posture or meditation as described in Chapters 3 to 10. We often begin with something concrete.
  □ Here are some examples:
    - Being mindful of breathing
    - Being mindful of a sitting or standing posture
    - Observing one thing such as a color, a sensation, or an image
- Provide instruction.
- Have the clients do the exercise for several minutes.
- When the time is up, ask, "How was that for you?"
  □ Let them share what they experienced. People are often eager to tell you.
  □ Find out if they felt they could do it.
  □ What difficulties, if any, did they have?
  □ Be willing to receive feedback so that you can individualize a posture or a meditation.
- Accept your clients' responses, whatever they are.
  □ Use the logic of errorless learning: Look for what is right in what the client does rather than what is wrong.
  □ This gives them an experience of mastery, one of the nonspecific healing factors observed in psychotherapy research (Frank, 1992).

- Here are some special considerations for different kinds of problems:
  □ Allow clients to keep their eyes open if they suffer from hallucinations, trauma, or delusions.
  □ For depressed clients, begin by teaching methods that focus attention on outer objects. They tend to be inwardly ruminating. Turning their attention outward can reduce their inner turmoil. This might also help them gain a sense of mastery.
  □ Anxious clients may feel more anxious when sitting still, so you might find it helpful to begin with a moving meditation. See Chapter 12 in the section "Calming Your Anxiety" on page 99-101, for instructions.
  □ Pick a meditation that addresses each client best. Think about how your client tends to use his or her attention, and notice what skills may need work. Choose a meditation that helps to correct any weakness. For example:
    ■ When clients are overly focused and tend to obsess about problems, use an open-focus mindfulness meditation.
    ■ When clients are unaware, impulsive, or out of touch, begin by directing attention to breathing, body awareness with simple postures, and mindful awareness of sitting, standing, and lying prone. As skills build, you can work with increasing their awareness of emotions, thoughts, and behaviors.

SPECIAL CONSIDERATIONS WHEN WORKING WITH SENIORS

The Man Who Reclaimed His Ability to Stand on His Own Two Feet

We often take for granted our ability to move and do things. But we should be sensitive to what our clients can and cannot do. We presented a meditation seminar at an elder care facility. An enthusiastic group enjoyed meditating and had many interesting thoughts and associations.

We introduced the "Discover Your Balance in Mountain Pose (Standing)" meditation (see Chapter 6, Figures 6.2 and 6.3, page 50). As we asked everyone to stand up, one of the men stood up and clutched his walker rail so tightly that his knuckles turned white. He said, "I am terrified to stand up. You know, I was a Holocaust survivor and endured many challenges in my life. But now, I can't even stand up by myself without feeling terrified of falling." We encouraged him to start from where he was, to hold his walker firmly as he swayed to discover his balance point. He practiced sincerely for a good 5 minutes, and eventually his grip relaxed. He even let go for several seconds and smiled. Afterward he shook our hand and said, "Thank you! You have given me new hope. I felt my confidence return for those moments and will practice what you have taught me!"

We learned from this brave man to never take anything for granted, even the simple act of standing upright. When working with seniors, be sensitive to their limitations, and yet, don't diminish your estimate of their potential. By careful, safe practice, even the oldest client can expand and grow.

Tips for Working with Seniors

- Seniors can do many of the yoga and mindfulness practices.
- Be aware of any physical or cognitive limitations when introducing yoga and mindfulness techniques.
- Always keep the safety of the client in mind.
- Start with what the client is capable of doing.
  □ Wheelchair asanas can be very helpful, invigorating, and fun!
  □ For those who are cognitively impaired, practice short meditations as brief as 30 seconds.
  □ Recognize when clients can do more, as many have great capacities and wisdom they can impart.
    ■ You are never too old or too ill to experience neuroplasticity (Gage, Eriksson, Perfilieva, & Bjork-Eriksson, 1998), so approach seniors with optimism.

WORKING WITH CHILDREN

Children are naturals for yoga and mindfulness. They love postures, can learn mindfulness methods, and enjoy the feeling of mastery they get from practicing meditation. The postures give them body awareness and can foster self-regulation. Mindfulness can help them gain control over aggression and acting out. By increasing control over attention, mindfulness has been shown to enhance learning and memory (Langer, 1989). Thus, students can benefit from the practice. In addition, yoga and mindfulness can be fun, especially if you present it in the right way.

Tips for Presenting Yoga and Mindfulness to Children and Adolescents

- Use any of the exercises in this workbook.
- Begin with a short amount of time, especially with young children.
- Start with something concrete, as in the exercises that follow.
- Make it fun! Children enjoy pretending, so use some of the animal postures.
- When working in a group, we often sit in a circle and share experiences after a meditation or yoga posture. Practice one meditation or posture as a group for a few minutes. Then go around the circle and encourage each child to describe what he or she experienced.
- Kids have vivid imaginations. Be supportive of their creative observations.

HELPING YOURSELF WITH STRESS AND BURNOUT

Yoga and mindfulness can help reduce therapist stress and burnout. Research shows that adding meditation to the daily routine will reduce stress and prevent burnout in health care professionals (Oman et al., 2006).

If you suspect that you might be suffering from too much stress and/or burnout, here is a simple checklist you can use. You may be experiencing stress and/or burnout if you answered always or sometimes to some of these items.

Practice the meditations in this section and then fill in the chart at the end of the chapter to monitor your progress.

FIGURE 16.1 Stress and Burnout Checklist

	Always	Sometimes	Never
Are you always exhausted and unable to be replenished even after a good night's sleep or weekend off?			
Do you feel bored when sitting in sessions?			
Are you consumed by your work, thinking about clients incessantly between sessions?			
Do you feel as if you can never get anything done or that you are always running behind?			
Are you neglecting your health: Missing sleep, not exercising, and/or eating poorly?			
Do you tend to avoid seeing people except when you have to?			
Do you feel frustrated or even annoyed by clients' problems?			
Do you feel as if you are incompetent or unable to handle your work?			
Are you turning to escapes such as drugs or alcohol?			

LETTING GO OF STRESS WHEN YOU CAN

The first place to begin when dealing with a stress problem, is to institute moments of relaxation and calm. Like the shoemaker who often went barefoot himself, we therapists are often so busy attending to our clients' needs, we might be neglectful of our own. You can nurture your own well-being in simple ways, and you will set a process in motion that will interrupt your stress pattern as you calm your over-activated nervous system. You might not feel the results immediately, but don't doubt yourself. Keep in mind that the nervous system does not turn on and off in an instant. Signals take time to readjust, and so you might not feel different until later. You have probably counseled your clients to be patient, so take your own advice!

Discovering Your Clear Consciousness

You have had times in your life when your mind was clear and your emotions were at peace. The potential is always there, just waiting to be expressed. Elicit your ability now.

Sit quietly and allow the flow of thoughts. Don't let yourself get carried away by any one thought. Just let thoughts flow by, like leaves moving along the current of a river. Stay in the moment without thinking anything in particular, but letting thoughts go. In time, moments without thought will occur. Allow this to develop naturally, as it will, as you sit quietly now. After some time with this meditation, you may discover that you can no longer find your disturbed mind.

Drawing on the Calm of Nature

Sometimes an outer situation can trigger inner calm. When you are trying to calm the troubled waters within, you may find that putting yourself into certain environments can bring an automatic response. You can facilitate this stimulus-response mechanism with mindfulness meditation in nature.

Meditate in Nature

Take a brief break. Go somewhere outdoors in nature, a local park, your own backyard, a beach, or a grassy area under a tree. If possible, sit down and let your thoughts settle. Listen to the sounds, feel the breeze, notice the temperature. Pay attention to the air as you breathe it into your body and then back out into the environment. Can you experience the ongoing exchange between you and the world without thinking anything beyond the experience itself? Take in the beauty you see and feel around you. Notice nature's perfect imperfection, how each blade of grass is different from the next, and yet shares common features. Sense the calm, quiet stability that is there in a tree, a bush, and a flower. Nature is always there to be seen and sensed, asking nothing from you. Breathe, look, and enjoy the moment. Your nervous system responds naturally as the stress reaction begins to fade.

Discover Your Clear Consciousness

Sit quietly and allow thoughts to flow. Don't let yourself get carried away by any one thought. Just allow thoughts to flow by, like leaves moving along the current on a river. Stay in the moment, without thinking anything in particular. In time, moments without thoughts will occur. Allow this to develop naturally, as it will, as you sit quietly. After some time with this meditation, you may find clarity and peace.

Meditation Traditions Provide New Schemas

Experienced psychologists have told us they felt bored when sitting with some of their clients. After years of practice, even you may find yourself occasionally feeling stale. You can gain new perspectives by considering the fascinating philosophies that created yoga and mindfulness practices. They offer a completely new way to look at reality, and thereby, inspire new ways of thinking.

Look at this illustration, the famous figure-ground experiment from Gestalt psychology. In Figure 16.2, do you see the vase? Or do you see the two faces? You can see each image at different times, depending on how you look at it.

FIGURE 16.2 Vase and Faces

Typically, we take for granted Aristotelian logic that states that either a thing is or is not. But according to Nagarjuna, the great Buddhist philosopher, a thing is, is not, neither, or both. Physics has come to this same conclusion. The theory of complementarity from particle physics has tried to understand our universe by looking at smaller and smaller particles. They found that the real essence of these very tiny particles isn't just material substance, nor is it just energy. In a sense it is neither and both simultaneously!

By opening up your thinking to these broader perspectives, you will see the world anew, and in the process look at clients' situations differently, to see possibilities you may not have considered. Please turn to our References, which includes helpful reading.

CHARTING

We encourage you to practice the many exercises offered in this workbook and use them to become your personal best. William James once advised us to act as if what you do makes a difference. It does. Yoga and mindfulness provide a means to shape our actions and those of others toward fulfillment, happiness, and well-being. Keep making small efforts and you will find, in time, things change in big ways for the better. Your work matters!

FIGURE 16.3 Shift Away from Stress and Burnout Checklist

	Always	Sometimes	Never
Are you always exhausted and unable to be replenished even after a good night's sleep or weekend off?			
Do you feel bored when sitting in sessions?			
Are you consumed by your work, thinking about clients incessantly between sessions?			
Do you feel as if you can never get anything done or that you are always running behind?			
Are you neglecting your health, missing sleep, not exercising, and/or eating poorly?			
Do you tend to avoid seeing people except when you have to?			
Do you feel frustrated or even annoyed by clients' problems?			
Do you feel as if you are incompetent or unable to handle your work?			
Are you using drugs or alcohol to escape your burdens?			
Do you devote time each day to yoga and mindfulness practice?			
Do you have periods of time when you feel optimistic, happy, and comfortable?			
Do you experience fulfillment and joy from your work?			

Conclusion

Each of the steps to attain Samadhi has been reasoned out, properly adjusted, and scientifically organized. When faithfully practiced, they will surely lead to the desired end. Then, will all sorrows cease, all miseries vanish. The seeds of action will be burnt, and the soul will be free forever.

—Vivekananda, 1953

We hope that yoga and mindfulness practice has set you on a healing path. We encourage you to maintain your mindful center and engage your mind, brain, and body to work together as you meet the demands of life. The innate wisdom of your deeper being is a resource to draw from, a wellspring for renewal.

Be willing to consider alternatives to your routines. Search within, and as the details emerge, take them seriously. Learn to sense what is needed, and permit it to develop. Discover new paths to follow for your unique individuality to develop. Then you will be better able to transform your life and make it what you want it to be.

We leave you now, with an invitation: Move into a comfortable posture and open your mindful eye. Look within and without, take a comfortable breath, and notice what you are experiencing right now. Carry this meditative awareness with you and call upon it whenever you need to, for healthy, happy, fulfilling living!

Breathe as you enter into the pose
Concentrate deeply, change flows
Leave the unchangeable past behind
Happiness begins now with an open mind!

—Annellen and C. Alexander Simpkins

References

Adler, K. A., & Deutsch, D. (1959). *Essays in individual psychology: Contemporary applications of Alfred Adler's theories.* New York, NY: Grove Press.

American Psychological Association, APA (2008). *Stress in America: Mind/Body Health: For a Healthy Mind and Body, Talk to a Psychologist, October 7, 2008.* Washington D.C.: American Psychological Association.

Bhatia, M., Kumar, A., Kumar, N., Pandey, R. M., & Kochupilla, V. (2003). Electrophysiologic evaluation of Sudarshan Kriaya: An EEG, BAER and P300 study. *Indian Journal of Pharmacology, 47,* 157–163.

Benson, H., & Wallace, R. (1972). Decreased drug abuse with transcendental meditation: A study of 1862 subjects. In C. J. Zarafonetis (Ed.), *Drug abuse: Proceedings of the International Conference.* Philadelphia, PA: Lea & Febiger.

Bowen, S., Witkiewitz, K., Dilworth, T. M., et al. (2006). Mindfulness meditation and substance use in an incarcerated population. *Psychology of Addictive Behaviors, 20*(3), 343–347.

Chan, W. T. (1963). *A source book in Chinese philosophy.* Princeton, NJ: Princeton University Press.

Dalai Lama, & Cutler, H. C. (1998). *The art of happiness.* New York, NY: Riverhead Books.

Desikachar, T. K. V. (1995). *The heart of yoga: Developing a personal practice.* Rochester, VT: Inner Traditions International.

Deutsch, E. (Trans.). (1968). *The Bhagavad Gita.* New York, NY: Holt, Rinehart, & Winston.

Dhar, H. L. (2002). Meditation, health, intelligence and performance. APICON *Medicine Update, 202,* 1376–1379.

Dillbeck, M. C., Cavanaugh, K. L., Glenn, T., et al. (1987). Consciousness as a field: The transcendental meditation and TM Sidhi program and changes in social indicators. *Journal of Mind and Behavior, 8,* 67104.

Dillbeck, M. C., & Orme-Johnson, D. W. (1987). Physiological differences between transcendental meditation and rest. *American Psychologist, 42*(9), 879–881.

Farb, N. A., Anderson, A. K., Mayberg, H., et al. (2010). Minding one's emotions: Mindfulness training alters the neural expression of sadness. *Emotion, 10*(1), 25–33.

Frank, J. D., & Frank, J. B. (1991). *Persuasion and healing.* Baltimore, MD: Johns Hopkins University Press.

Gage, F. H., Eriksson, P. S., Perfilieva, E., & Bjork-Eriksson, T. (1998). Neurogenesis in the adult human hippocampus. *Nature Medicine, 4*(11), 1313–1317.

Gandhi, M. (1960). *An autobiography or the story of my experiments with truth.* Bombay, India: Ghandi Book Centre.

Granath, J., Ingvarsson, S., von Thiele, U., & Lundberg, U. (2006). Stress management: A randomized study of cognitive behavioral therapy and yoga therapy. *Cognitive Behavior Therapy, 35*(1), 3–10.

Green, E., Green, A., & Walters, E. (1970). Voluntary control of internal states: Psychological and physiological. *Journal of Transpersonal Psychology, 1*, 1–26.

Hagelin, J. S., Rainforth, M. V., Cavanaugh, K., et al. (1999). Effects of group practice of the transcendental meditation program on preventing violent crime in Washington, D.C.: Results of the national demonstration project, June–July, 1993. *Social Indicators Research, 47*(2), 153–201.

Hotzel, B. K., Carmody, J., Vangel, M., et al. (2011). Mindfulness practice leads to increases in regional brain gray matter density. *Psychiatry Research: Neuroimaging, 191*(1), 36–43.

Hotzel, B. K. (2007). Differential engagement of anterior cingulate and adjacent medial frontal cortex in adept meditator and non-meditators. *Neuroscience Letters, 421*, 16–21.

Hugdahl, K. (1996). Brain laterality—beyond the basics. *European Psychologist, 1*, 206–220.

James, W. (1896). *The principles of psychology.* New York, NY: Henry Holt & Co.

James, W. (1917). *Selected papers on philosophy.* London, England: J. M. Dent & Sons.

Johnstone, T., van Reekum, C., Urry, H., et al. (2007). Failure to regulate: Counterproductive recruitment of top-down prefrontal subcortical circuitry in major depression. *Journal of Neuroscience, 27*, 8877–8884.

Janata, P., Tomic, S. T., & Haberman, J. M. (2012). Sensorimotor coupling in music and the psychology of the groove. *Journal of Experimental Psychology-General, 141*(1), 54–75.

Kjaer, T. W., Bertelsen, C., Piccini, P., et al. (2002). Increased dopamine tone during meditation-induced change of consciousness. *Brain Research: Cognitive Brain Research, 13*(2), 255–259.

Khumar, S. S., Kaur, P., & Kaur, S. (1993). Effectiveness of Shavasana on depression among university students. *Indian Journal of Clinical Psychology, 20*(2), 82–87.

Krishnamurti, J. (1968). *The first and last freedom.* Wheaton, IL: The Theosophical Publishing House.

Kushner, K. (2000). *One arrow, one life: Zen, archery, enlightenment.* Boston, MA: Tuttle Publishing.

Langer, E. J. (1989). *Mindfulness.* Cambridge, MA: Da Capo Press.

Lazar, S. W., Kerr, C. E., Wasserman, R. H., et al. (2005). Meditation experience is associated with increased cortical thickness. *NeuroReport, 16*(17), 1893–1897.

Michalsen, A., Grossman, P., Acil, A., et al. (2005). Yoga reduces stress and anxiety among distressed women. *Medical Science Monitor, 11*(12), 555–561.

Meichenbaum, D. (2012). *Roadmap to resilience: A guide for military, trauma victims, and their families*. Clearwater, FL: Institute Press.

Miller, B. S. (1995). *Yoga discipline of freedom: The Yoga Sutras attributed to Patanjali*. New York, NY: Bantam Books.

Oman, D., Hedberg, J., & Thoresen, C. (2006). Passage meditation reduces perceived stress in health professionals: A randomized controlled trial. *Journal of Consulting and Clinical Psychology, 74*(4), 714–719.

Porges, S. W. (2011). *The Polyvagal theory*. New York, NY: W. W. Norton & Company.

Prasad, K. V. V., Sunita, M., Raju, P. S., et al. (2006). Impact of pranayama and yoga on lipid profile in normal healthy volunteers. *Journal of Exercise Physiology Online, 9*, 1–6.

Radhakrishnan. (1977). *Indian philosophy*. Vol. I & II. London: George Allen & Unwin Ltd.

Reps, P. (1980). *Zen flesh, Zen bones: A collection of Zen and pre-Zen writings*. Rutland, VT: Charles E. Tuttle, Co.

Ressler, K., & Mayberg, H. (2007). Targeting abnormal neural circuits in mood and anxiety disorders: From the laboratory to the clinic. *Nature Neuroscience, 10*, 1116–1124.

Sarang, S. P., & Telles, S. (2006). Changes in P300 following two yoga-based relaxation techniques. *International Journal of Neuroscience, 116*(12), 1419–1430.

Shapiro, D., Cook, I. A., Davydov, D. M., et al. (2007). Yoga as a complementary treatment of depression: Effects of traits and moods on treatment outcomes. *Evidence-based Complementary and Alternative Medicine*. doi: http://10.1093/ecam/nel114

Simpkins, C. A., & Simpkins, A. M. (1999). *Simple Zen: A guide to living day by day*. Boston, MA: Tuttle Publishing.

Simpkins, C. A., & Simpkins, A. M. (2000). *Simple Buddhism: A guide to enlightened living*. Boston. MA: Tuttle Publishing.

Simpkins, C. A., & Simpkins, A. M. (2001). *Simple Tibetan Buddhism: A guide to tantric living*. Boston, MA: Tuttle Publishing.

Simpkins, C. A., & Simpkins, A. M. (2003). *Yoga basics*. Boston, MA: Tuttle Publishing.

Simpkins, C. A., & Simpkins, A. M. (2007). *Meditation from thought to action with audio CD*. San Diego, CA: Radiant Dolphin Press.

Simpkins, C. A., & Simpkins, A. M. (2009). *Meditation for therapists and their clients*. New York, NY: W. W. Norton & Co.

Simpkins, C. A., & Simpkins, A. M. (2010). *The Dao of neuroscience: Combining Eastern and Western principles for optimal therapeutic change*. New York, NY: W. W. Norton & Co.

Simpkins, C. A., & Simpkins, A. M. (2010). *Meditation and yoga in psychotherapy: Techniques for clinical practice*. Hoboken, NJ: John Wiley & Sons.

Simpkins, C. A., & Simpkins, A. M. (2011). *Zen meditation in psychotherapy: Techniques for clinical practice*. Hoboken, NJ: John Wiley & Sons.

Sinh, P. (Trans.). (2013, October 28). *Hatha Yoga Pradipika*. Retrieved from http://www.sacredtexts.com/hin/hyp/index.htm

Stanislavski, C. (1977). *Building a character*. New York, NY: Theatre Art Books.

Streeter, C. C., Jensen, J. E., Perimutter, R. M., et al. (2007). Yoga asana sessions increase brain GABA levels: a pilot study. *Journal of Alternative Complementary Medicine, 13*(4), 419–426.

Suzuki, D. T. (1973). *Zen and Japanese culture.* Princeton, NJ: Princeton University Press.

Suzuki, S. (1979). *Zen mind, beginner's mind: Informal talks on Zen meditation and practice.* New York, NY: Weatherhill.

Tang, Y-Y., Lu, Q., Geng, X., et al. (2010). Short-term meditation induces white matter changes in the anterior cingulate. *Proceedings of the National Academy of Sciences, 107*(35), 15649–15652.

Tang, Y-Y., Ma, Y., Fan, Y., et al. (2009). Central and autonomic nervous system interaction is altered by short-term meditation. *Proceedings of the National Academy of Sciences, 106*(22), 8865–8870.

Tang, Y-Y., & Posner, M. (2012, July 11). Chinese mindfulness meditation prompts double positive punch in brain white matter. *Proceedings of the National Academy of Sciences.* Retrieved from http://medicalxpress.com/news/2012-06-chinese-meditation-ibmt-prompts-positive.html

Travis, F., & Shear, J. (2010). Focused attention, open monitoring and automatic self-transcending: Categories to organize meditations from Vedic, Buddhist and Chinese traditions. *Consciousness and Cognition*, 19, 1110–1119.

Uebelacker, L. A., Epstein-Lubow, G., Gaudiano, B. A., et al. (2010). Hatha yoga for depression: Critical review of the evidence for efficacy, plausible mechanisms of action, and directions for future research. *Journal of Psychiatric Practice, 16*(1), 22–23.

Vaitl, D., & Ott, U. (2005). Altered states of consciousness induced by psychophysiological techniques. *Mind and Matter, 3*, 9–30.

Vivekananda, S. (1953). Vivekananda: *The yogas and other works.* New York, NY: Ramakrishna-Vivekananda Center.

Weng, H. Y., Fox, A. S., Shackman, A. J., et al. (2013). Compassion training alters altruism and neural responses to suffering. *Psychological Science, 24*(7), 1171–1180.

Williams, A. L., Selwyn, P. A., Liberti, L., et al. (2005). Efficacy of frequent mantram repetition on stress, quality of life, and spiritual well-being in veterans: A pilot study. *Journal of Palliative Medicine, 5*, 939–952.

About the Authors

C. Alexander Simpkins, Ph.D., and Annellen M. Simpkins, Ph.D., are psychologists specializing in neuroscience, psychotherapy, meditation, and hypnosis. The Simpkins are authors of 29 books, many of them best sellers, including *Neuroscience for Clinicians* (Springer, 2012), *The Dao of Neuroscience* (Norton, 2010), and *Neuro-Hypnosis* (Norton, 2010). They have also written about meditation for healthy mind-brain change: *The Tao of Bipolar Disorder* (New Harbinger, 2013), *Zen Meditation in Psychotherapy* (Wiley, 2012), *Meditation and Yoga in Psychotherapy: Techniques for Clinical Practice* (Wiley, 2011), and *Meditation for Therapists and Their Clients* (Norton, 2009). Their books have more than 20 foreign editions and have won numerous awards.

Drs. Simpkins have been practicing psychotherapy for more than three decades and have taught their meditative and hypnotic methods to facilitate mind-brain change to people of all ages. They have been involved in neuroscience for 15 years and have been integrating it into treatments and helping to bring the most recent research findings to practitioners. They present seminars at professional conferences, state mental hospitals, university campuses, and to popular and professional audiences around the world. They have performed psychotherapy research and are currently doing a neuroscience study of unconscious movement. They studied with psychotherapy masters, including Milton H. Erickson, Jerome D. Frank, Carl Rogers, Lawrence Kubie, and Ernest Rossi, and neuroscience innovators, including Vilayanur Ramachandran, Jaime Pineda, Paul and Patricia Churchland, Stephen Anagnostaras, and William Bechtel. Their Eastern philosophy influence along with their commitment to continual learning and therapeutic effectiveness has helped them to see therapy through the crystal of a unique vision, which they bring to you with warmth and clarity in their books and seminars.